FIRST EDITI

Congratulations!

You now have the "tool-kit" to build an Outstanding Consulting Engineering Practice. I wish you much success.

Jack Gaskell

The **"Complete Guide"** to

CONSULTING ENGINEERING

How To Start & Manage An Outstanding
Consulting Engineering Practice

John D. Gaskell
Retired Professional Engineer

Professional Value Books, Inc.
110 Shore Court, Unit 304, North Palm Beach, FL 33408
TheEngineersResource.com

The Complete Guide to CONSULTING ENGINEERING

International Standard Book Numbers (ISBN)
Softcover: 978-0-9905120-0-4
Hardcover: 978-09905120-4-2
E-Book: 978-0-9905120-1-1

Proofreader: JERA Publishing (Brooke Payne)
Interior Designer: JERA Publishing (Stephanie Anderson)
EBook Conversion: JERA Publishing (Jason Orr)
Cover Designer: JERA Publishing (Jason Orr)

Publisher: Professional Value Books, Inc., http://TheEngineersResource.com
110 Shore Court, Unit 304, North Palm Beach, FL 33408 U.S.A.

Library of Congress Control Number: 2014948379

DEDICATION

This book is dedicated to the memory of John W. King, PE, my mentor, my partner, my friend, and the most honest and generous man that I have ever known.

This book is also dedicated to the memory of my wife, Patricia M. Gaskell (Levesque), the love of my life, the mother of my children, and the smartest person that I have ever known.

They are both missed by many.

Lastly, this book is also dedicated to Jillian Rose Butler, who grows more adorable, beautiful, bright, and special every day. And I would say these things even if she were not my favorite (only) granddaughter.

FOREWORD

In his *Complete Guide to Consulting Engineering*, Jack Gaskell provides readers with a dose of wisdom that can't be had by just Googling on the Internet. Jack possesses a rare combination of business acumen and engineering knowledge which made his career a success and, now, his writing of value. In the book, he is offering those just entering the profession the benefits of a lifetime of experience and hard-learned lessons. Numerous amusing real-world anecdotes add color and readability to the text. Jack teaches readers certain essential skills that are timeless—these do not change with technology: how to treat clients in various situations, the art of professional selling, and making intelligent back-office decisions. The book is a must read for the young consultant and a perfect reference guide for experienced engineers.

James R. Fink, PE, Kleinholz Inc., Consulting & Forensic Engineers
kleinholzinc.com

ACKNOWLEDGMENTS

FOR AUTHORIZATION TO WRITE THIS BOOK:
Thomas E. Lent, President and CEO of Thielsch Engineering, Inc., for relieving me of the "non-disclosure" requirements of our purchase and sale agreement when Thielsch Engineering purchased Gaskell Associates, Ltd. I am also grateful to Tom for the professional way that he treated me while I served as one of his Division Presidents, his friendship, and his encouragement in writing this book.

FOR GATHERING INFORMATION:
When I retired from Thielsch Engineering, I had no plans to write a book and did not take copies of anything. But former employees and clients were willing to search through the archives to provide information that was greatly helpful.

Joe Beretta, Bob Bravo, Greg Driggers, Jim Fink, Roger Harris, Gary Hebner, Dana Newbrook, Jackie Rand, and Duncan Speel.

FOR PREPARING THE COVER BACKGROUND:
Evan Oliveira and Francesco Bianco

FOR REVIEWING & EDITING MY CHAPTER ON "FORENSIC ENGINEERING," and for much advice and encouragement over the years as a colleague and friend.

Marvin M. Specter, PE, LS, PP, F.NAFE, F.ITE, F.NSPE, Executive Director Emeritus of the National Academy of Forensic Engineers (NAFE).

FOR REVIEWING MY MANUSCRIPT:
Several people generously gave their time to review and provide constructive advice that greatly improved the final publication of this book.

Joseph R. Beretta, President and CEO, The RGB Corporation; Michelle, Daniel, Danny, and Jillian Butler; Robert C. Bravo, PE, Griffith and Vary, Inc.; Pamela M. Cox; Raymond A. DeCesare, AIA, retired; James R. Fink, PE, Kleinholz, Inc., Consulting & Forensic Engineers; John T. Gaskell, ESQ.; Gary Hebner, Senior Commissioning Agent, Stephen Turner, Inc.; Dana M. Newbrook, AIA, NCARB, a i designs, Ltd.; Matthew J. Viana, PE, Senior Engineer, Millstone Engineering, P.C.; and Robert Steven Wilkinson, PE, Wilkinson Associates, Inc.

ABOUT THE AUTHOR

John D. Gaskell is a retired consulting engineer who wishes to share his 35 years of experience with both young engineers thinking of starting their own practice and those old hands who wish to improve their results.

In essence, Jack's readers discover "step-by-step" how to start and manage an *"outstanding"* engineering practice and exactly how to gain a reputation as an expert in their specialty.

He was President of Gaskell Associates Consulting Engineers, now a Division of Thielsch Engineering, Inc. Jack is a graduate of Wentworth Institute, with an associate's degree in Electrical Engineering Technology, and the University of Rhode Island, with a Bachelor of Science degree in Electrical Engineering.

Jack was a member of the following professional organizations: Rhode Island Society of Professional Engineers, Providence Engineering Society, Electrical League of Rhode Island, Illuminating Engineering Society of North America, National Electromagnetic Field Testing Association, and the National Academy of Forensic Engineers.

He is a past President of the Rhode Island Society of Professional Engineers, past President of the Rhode Island Chapter of the Illuminating Engineering Society, past Director of the Electrical League of Rhode Island, and past Chairman of the Electrical Code Sub-Committee of the Rhode Island Building Code Standards Committee.

Jack was honored by being selected "Engineer of the Year" by the Rhode Island Society of Professional Engineers; "Man of the Year" by the Electrical League of Rhode Island; and "Freeman Award" recipient by the Providence Engineering Society for the purpose of recognizing major achievements in engineering.

He spends winters at his home in North Palm Beach, FL, enjoying the warm weather and losing at the game of pool. Summers are spent at his home in Warwick, RI, enjoying his children, grandchildren, and many great friends.

Jack also has three other books under way. Look for them!

GUARANTEE

The publisher is so convinced that you will be 100% satisfied with this book that we provide a full money back, no questions asked guarantee. Just notify the publisher at Professional Value Books, Inc., 110 Shore Court, Unit 304, North Palm Beach, FL 33408, provided that you purchased the book from the website: TheEngineersResource.com.

DISCLAIMER

The author, John D. Gaskell, is a retired/inactive/no longer licensed engineer. He feels qualified to tell you how he started and managed his consulting engineering practice and to give general advice. But he is not an attorney, accountant, insurance expert, or any other kind of business professional and can only give general guidance, which should always be confirmed by an attorney or other appropriate professionals before proceeding. He has expended considerable effort in the preparation of his books, articles, and blogs. He believes, to the best of his knowledge, that the information contained therein is accurate. Nothing should be construed as legal advice, and he offers his apologies, in advance, for the inevitable blunders.

CONTENTS

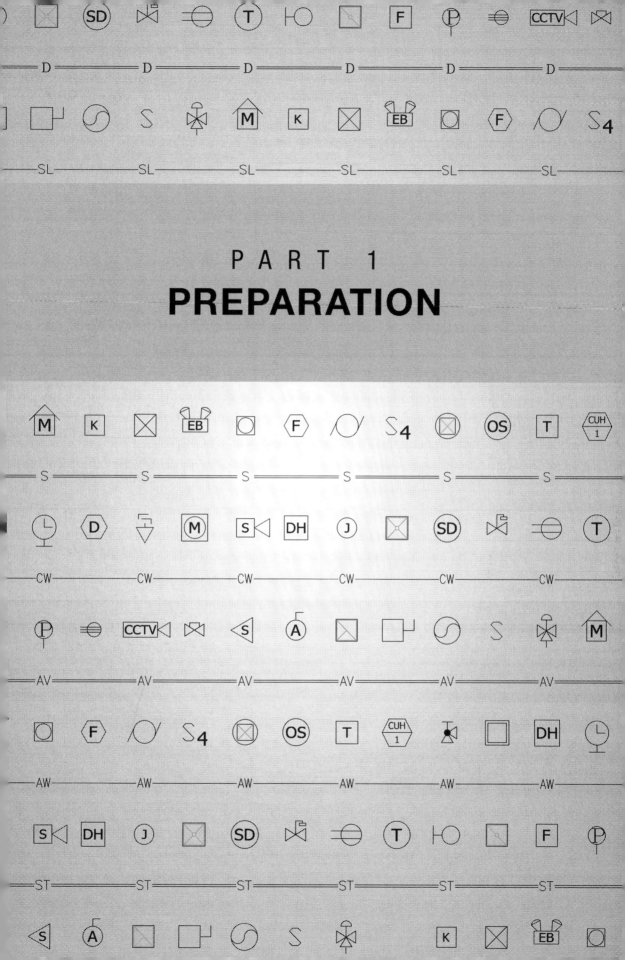

PART 1
PREPARATION

BECOMING A PROFESSIONAL ENGINEER

INTRODUCTION

Learn about the exciting field of consulting engineering and how to determine if this is the right career choice for you. Discover step-by-step how to become a licensed professional engineer, including educational requirements, experience, and examinations. Find out the benefits and drawbacks of consulting engineering as well as the advantages and disadvantages of owning your own practice.

WHAT IS AN ENGINEER?

The Merriam-Webster dictionary defines an engineer as "a person who has scientific training and who designs and builds complicated products, machines, systems, or structures." At the high school level, students should consider career options. Don't choose a career just because it "sounds like fun." Make sure that it will be lucrative enough to support you and a family, will not restrict where you can live, and will not require odd hours or excessive travel. *I have a friend whose daughter became a Marine Biologist and later found out that it qualified her to "shovel seal poop."* Those who are strong in science and mathematics should consider engineering.

However, before spending four years of your life and your parents' hard earned money, you should be reasonably sure that engineering is for you. I recommend "shadowing" an engineer of the discipline that interests you. If you don't know an engineer, use the internet. Try structural engineers (for example) or professional engineers. Make a phone call, and explain that you are a high school student interested in becoming an engineer and would like to speak to an engineer. Explain to the engineer that you would like to come to his or her office and observe a typical day. Very few engineers would turn down that kind of a request, and it might turn into a summer internship or a job after graduation. If you are unsure of your discipline of choice, call engineers of various specialties to try and gain an understanding of what their job entails. Spending time with several engineers would broaden your perceptive.

In my case, my father was an electrician. I helped him with side jobs and grew-up with an interest in electricity. I chose to take an academic vocational course in high school, Radio–Television and Industrial Electronics, with the goal of becoming a TV Repair Man. (Do you know anyone, today, who is making a living repairing TVs?) In my Senior Year of high school, two of my classmates decided to go to Wentworth Institute in Boston, MA, for an associate's degree in Electrical Engineering; so, I applied and was accepted. When my two years at Wentworth were almost complete, a friend in my class told me that he was going to a four year college for a Bachelor of Science Degree in Electrical Engineering while getting almost two years of credit for his associate's degree. So, I applied at the University of Rhode Island and was accepted . . . but with no credits for the two years at Wentworth. However, low in-state tuition and the ability to commute from home made this the only realistic option for me.

Instead of "stumbling" your way through six years to become an engineer, plan ahead and do it in four years. In high school, take a college prep course that is strong in science and higher mathematics.

When selecting a college, make sure that it is accredited by the "Accreditation Board for Engineering Technology–Engineering Accreditation Commission" (ABET-EAC). Surprisingly, some good colleges are not. (See why later in this chapter.)

WHAT IS A PROFESSIONAL ENGINEER?

www.ask.com answers as follows:

> "A Professional Engineer (PE in the U.S.) is one who has attained a credential that permits him to provide engineering services to the general public."

WHAT IS A CONSULTING ENGINEER?

www.ask.com answers as follows:

> "Consulting engineers are individuals who, because of training in one or more engineering specialties, are licensed professional engineers in private practice. They serve private and public clients in ways ranging from brief consultations to complete design and coordination of projects. They are often the technical liaison between architects, process specialists, contractors, suppliers and the client. A consulting engineer can provide general consultation, feasibility reports, design, cost estimates, rate studies, project development, patent assistance, and preparation of environmental impact statements."

Those who offer their services to the public as an engineer are required to be licensed as a "Registered Professional Engineer." In each state, registration is governed by a "Board of Registration of Professional Engineers" who review/approve qualifications, administer tests, and oversee practices. In Rhode Island, the board is called "The Board of Design Professionals" and is made up of multi-professionals (engineers, architects, and land surveyors). Each state's board has its own governing rules, but the same national tests are administered in each state. Basically, the requirements are as follows:

- Be a graduate of an ABET-EAC accredited engineering program of four (4) years or more.
- Pass an eight (8) hour written examination called the "Fundamentals in Engineering" (FE) examination.
- A minimum of four (4) years of experience in engineering work working under the supervision of a Professional Engineer.
- Pass an eight (8) hour written examination called the "Professional Engineer" (PE) examination in the principles and practice of engineering.

Some boards modify these requirements, usually based on experience. Most allow candidates to take the "fundamentals" exam in their senior year of college while the calculus, chemistry, etc. are still relatively fresh in their memory.

To qualify to take the PE exam, it is important that there is a professional engineer at your place of employment who is willing to "certify" that your experience in engineering work was "of a grade and character which indicates that you may be competent to practice engineering."

At least 6 months before you take the PE exam, you should start studying. One option is to go to the website of the National Council of Examiners for Engineering and Surveying (NCEES) and refer to practice exams (http://nceet. org/exams/pe-exam/). Both the FE and PE exams are "open-book." Refer to the website for details. An additional option is to purchase a study guide, which can be found advertised in engineering magazines and now on the internet. They usually include examples of previous exam questions. Many colleges of engineering offer continuing education courses to prepare you for either the FE or the PE exam.

Your daily work is typically restricted to a very small segment of your specialty. The PE exam, however, is very broad. Therefore, you must prepare yourself for a range of questions beyond your actual work experience. Electrical engineering, for example, includes (but is not limited to) electrical design for buildings, power transmission and distribution, electronic circuit design, and many other specialized areas. Sometimes, it is possible (for an added fee) to have a special exam prepared for you in your narrow specialty, but your registration will be restricted to that narrow area.

After I passed the PE exam, I was registered as a professional engineer, which meant that I could certify (attach my PE seal/stamp) to any type of engineering documents, as long as I was willing to show competence in that area of engineering. In recent years, engineers are registered in one or more standard engineering specialties and their practice is limited to that area of work. These standard specialties include:

- Agricultural
- Architectural
- Chemical
- Civil: Construction
- Civil: Geotechnical
- Civil: Structural
- Civil: Transportation
- Civil: Water Resources and Environmental
- Control Systems
- Electrical and Computer: Computer Engineering
- Electrical and Computer: Electrical and Electronics
- Electrical and Computer: Power
- Environmental
- Fire Protection
- Industrial
- Mechanical: HVAC and Refrigeration
- Mechanical: Mechanical Systems and Materials
- Mechanical: Thermal and Fluids Systems

- Metallurgical and Materials
- Mining and Mineral Processing
- Naval Architecture and Marine
- Nuclear

- Petroleum
- Software
- Structural

REGISTRATION LAWS

All states require licensure to practice engineering. For instance, Rhode Island's law states the following:

> **§ 5-8-1 Registration required for practice of engineering.** – In order to safeguard life, health, and property, and to promote the public welfare, the practice of engineering in this state is declared to be subject to regulation in the public interest. It is unlawful for any person to practice, or to offer to practice, engineering in this state, as defined in the provisions of this chapter, or to use in connection with his or her name or otherwise assume, or advertise any title or description tending to convey the impression that he or she is an engineer unless that person has been registered or exempted under the provisions of this chapter. The right to engage in the practice of engineering is deemed a personal right, based on the qualifications of the individual as evidenced by his or her certificate of registration, which is not transferable.

You need to investigate the requirements of each state in which you plan to do business. Just because you are registered in one state, don't assume that you will be able to get registered in all states.

Most states offer "reciprocity," acceptance of another state's PEs, without requiring an additional examination. As an example, Rhode Island's law states the following:

> **§ 5-8-11 General requirements for registration or certification.**
> (1) As a professional engineer:
> *(i) Registration by endorsement.* (A) A person holding a current certificate of registration to engage in the practice of engineering, on the basis of comparable written examinations, issued to him or her by either a proper authority of a state, territory, or possession of the United States, the District of Columbia, or of any foreign country, and

whose qualifications meets the requirements of this chapter, based on verified evidence may, upon application, be registered without further examination.

Be sure that you research the most current version of the laws, usually available on-line.

Most states require that each entity that practices or offers to practice engineering must hold a current Certificate of Authorization (COA). Make sure that your firm (whether sole proprietorship, corporation, partnership, or LLC) has a current COA. For instance, Rhode Island's law states the following:

§ 5-8-24 Sole proprietorship, partnership, limited liability partnership, corporate and limited liability company. – (a) The practice or offer to practice engineering as defined by this chapter by a sole proprietorship, partnership, limited liability partnership, corporation or a limited liability company subsequently referred to as the "firm," through individuals is permitted; provided, that the individuals: (1) are in direct control of the practice; (2) exercise personal supervision of all personnel who act in behalf of the firm in professional and technical matters; and (3) are registered under the provisions of this chapter; and provided, that the firm has been issued a certificate of authorization by the board of engineers.

(b)(1) Within one year after enactment of this chapter, every firm must obtain a certificate of authorization from the board and those individuals in direct control of the practice and who exercise direct supervision of all personnel who act in behalf of the firm in professional and technical matters must be registered with the board. The certificate of authorization shall be issued by the board upon satisfaction of the provisions of this chapter and the payment of a fee not to exceed one hundred fifty dollars ($150). This fee is waived if the firm consists of only one person who is the person in responsible charge.

(2) Every firm desiring a certificate of authorization must file with the board an application for a certificate of authorization on a form to be provided by the board. A separate form provided by the board shall be filed with each renewal of the certificate of authorization and within thirty (30) days of the time any information previously filed with the board has changed, is no longer true or valid, or has been

revised for any reason. If, in its judgment, the information contained on the application and renewal form is satisfactory and complete, the board will issue a certificate of authorization for the firm to practice engineering in this state.

(3) No firm that has been granted a certificate of authorization by the board shall be relieved of responsibility for modification or derivation of the certificate, unless the board has issued for the applicant a certificate of authorization or a letter indicating the eligibility of the applicant to receive the certificate. The firm applying shall supply the certificate or letter from the board with its application for incorporation, organization or registration as a foreign corporation.

DO YOU WANT TO BE A "CONSULTING ENGINEER"?

Benefits

- Interesting Work – Each project is unique with specific requirements, existing conditions, options, and cost constraints.
- Participation in all aspects – You create (your engineering specialty of) a project from the study through design, approvals, bidding, shop drawings, clarifications, construction observations, and the final "punch list." You actually see the project go from a blank sheet of paper to a constructed, one of a kind project that you can see and touch.
- Not stuck behind a desk – Some of your day will be made up of meetings with clients, vendors, colleagues, utility companies, contractors, and others, field investigations, and job site observations.

Drawbacks

- You are in an adversarial position – Your oversight of a project is to make sure that the owner gets the equivalent of what you specified. The contractor typically wants you to accept an inferior product, your client expects you to protect the building owner's interest, and the owner often wants better than what you specified.

- The Construction Industry is "cyclical" – If you're good at your job, you will usually be working. But if a recession is too deep or lasts too long, you may find yourself unemployed.
- Deadline Pressure – Deadlines are constantly changing and often there are multiple projects pressing you for attention. Overtime and sorting out the top priorities can be stressful.
- Profitably Pressure – Everyone in business is driven by a profit motive, even consulting engineering firms. No matter how good that you are at your job, if you can't make a profit for the company, you will not last.
- Too Much Work – Consulting engineering firms are reluctant to turn down projects because they can never tell when current projects will be delayed and they may have spent a year or more waiting for a project that suddenly gets the go-ahead. That creates more stress for you.
- Too Little Work – Conversely, too little work is even more stressful; it almost never seems like the work load is steady.
- You're the "bad guy" – During construction, the owner sees you occasionally but usually sees the contractor every day, and friendships are formed. Before you know it, in protecting the owner's interest, you are being too hard on his friend.

DO YOU WANT TO OWN YOUR OWN ENGINEERING PRACTICE?

Advantages:

- You have a much higher earning potential.
- Pride of ownership.
- Benefits of being the boss.
- You get to make all the final decisions.
- You can't get laid-off.
- You get to keep the profits.
- You can pick and choose the most appealing projects to personally handle and assign the others to your staff.
- You can pursue the most interesting/profitable projects.
- You spend time socializing with clients and potential clients.
- If you are successful and hire an able staff, you will have a valuable asset to sell when it comes time for your retirement.

Disadvantages:

- Be prepared to make "Sacrifices" – *When I was new in business and still operating alone, work slowed down, and my wife and I decided to take a quick driving vacation to Canada. At the last minute, I got a call from my biggest client announcing that he had just promised a client of his to provide a redesign that had to be delivered in one week. It was no fun having to go out to the car to break the bad news to my wife and two small children.*
- You make the "Firing Decisions" – This is particularly hard during the holiday season.
- The losses are all yours – On average, I made about three times more compensation than my fellow engineering classmates, but, during one recession, I lost more than my salary for three years in a row.
- Employees – The biggest headache in running any business is managing human resources. Often, employees don't get along with each other or with the clients, and, sometimes, they don't even care about the success of the company that employs them. Regardless, before you know it, you may be responsible for thirty or more mouths to feed. That is an awesome and burdensome responsibility.

OUTLINE SUMMARY

- **Consider engineering:** Those who have good science and mathematical grades and interests should consider engineering.

- **Shadow:** Spend a day with an engineer of the discipline that interests you.

- **College selection:** Make sure that the college of your choice is ABET-EAC accredited.

- **FE exam:** In your senior year of college, take the FE written examination in the fundamentals of engineering.

- **Gain experience:** A minimum of four (4) years of "certifiable" experience in engineering work is required to be eligible to take the PE exam.

- **PE exam:** Take the PE exam as soon as you are eligible. Not everyone passes the first time. Don't give up.

- **Know the laws:** Comply with the Professional Registration Laws in all the states where you will practice.

- **Consider consulting engineering:** Carefully ponder the pros and cons of being a "consulting engineer":
  - Benefits: Full involvement with all aspects of interesting projects while not being tied to a desk.
  - Drawbacks: Being in an adversarial position in a cyclical industry, the stress of deadlines, the pressure to be profitable, and the dilemma of either too much or too little work.

- **Consider ownership:** Carefully mull over the pros and cons of "owning" a consulting engineering practice:
  - Benefits: Making all of the final decisions; never being laid-off; keeping all of the profits; and being able to sell a valuable asset upon retirement.
  - Drawbacks: Personal and family sacrifices; difficulty of dealing with employees and acceptance of any losses.

PREPARING FOR YOUR OWN FIRM

INTRODUCTION

Don't just "stumble" into becoming a consulting engineer. Plan for it. Learn how to systematically search for and get the right job in a consulting engineering firm, one that will qualify you to take the PE exam and give you the knowledge and experience to eventually head-up your own firm. Detect the secrets of being properly prepared for your job interview. Discover how to become an "exceptional" employee, and see how that will help you when you start your own "outstanding" engineering practice.

Find out how easy it is to transcend from the status of a "nobody" to being "widely known and respected." Uncover the mysteries of getting elected "unopposed" to Engineering Society Boards and being nominated for prestigious awards. With determination and effort, you can establish credentials that will eventually distinguish you from your competitors. The important lesson here is: "It doesn't just happen—you make it happen." Read how!

MY START

As with education, I kind of "stumbled" into consulting engineering. In my senior year at URI, I happened to have lunch with a classmate who told me of an interesting summer job that he had working for a consulting engineer. I asked: "What is a consulting engineer?" He told me that the job entailed drafting for an electrical professional engineer who provided consulting services to architects.

He further explained that architects hire engineers to draw system plans and write specifications for their buildings, including (but not limited to) electrical, mechanical (heating, ventilating, air conditioning, and plumbing), fire protection (sprinklers), structural, and civil. Also, sometimes very narrow specialties are required, such as acoustical engineering. Electrical systems include: utilities serving the building (power, telephone, data, cable TV, and fire alarm), lighting, power distribution, fire alarm systems, telephone distribution, cable TV distribution, and any other electrical system that the particular building might require.

The consulting engineer is responsible for designing within the architect's budget limitations and coordinating with the requirements of utility companies and inspection authorities. At the end of the design phase, the consultant prepares a specification document detailing the electrical material requirements and system functions. During bidding, he attends pre-bid meetings, clarifies electrical issues, and prepares addenda for the architect to issue to inform bidders of changes in the requirements. After a contract is awarded, the consultant reviews/approves shop drawings detailing all equipment that the contractor proposes. During the construction phase, he visits the job site to record progress and clarifies the contract documents. At the completion of the construction phase, he prepares a "punch-list" detailing corrections to the work, if needed.

This accidental conversation set me on a path to becoming a consulting engineer. I sent a resume to each of the three electrical engineers listed in the local Yellow Pages and to several of the local architects. One of the architectural firms was utilizing an electrical engineer that was consulting to them on an "hourly-basis." He was reviewing the plans prepared by one of the staff architects, then preparing the specifications. This electrical engineer was approaching retirement, so they hired me to learn from him and succeed him as their "in-house" electrical engineer upon his retirement.

Fortunately for me, this electrical engineer, John W. King, PE, was one of the most knowledgeable and highly respected engineers in the State of Rhode Island. John started his career in the electrical industry teaching returning WW2 veterans electricity at a vocational school. He then worked as an electrical inspector, and when a local architect needed help with the electrical design of a complicated project, the architect called on John, thus starting his career as an electrical engineer. Later, when the state required licensing of engineers, he was granted PE Registration without an engineering degree and without an examination because of his experience and reputation. He was even appointed by the governor to serve on the Board of Registration of Professional Engineers from 1964 to 1975.

At some point, John opened up his own engineering office, providing services to many different architects and private clients (colleges, hospitals, building owners, etc.). Eventually, he became partners with a mechanical engineer.

When I introduced myself to Mr. King, he said: "Oh yes, my replacement." I don't remember my startled response, but we soon became good friends. It reminds me of Thomas Jefferson's reply when he was presented as US Ambassador to France: "I am merely Mr. Franklin's successor; no one could replace Mr. Franklin."

I worked for the architectural firm (while being trained by Mr. King) for about 1 ½ years. At that point, John and his partner notified the firm that John no longer had the time to consult to them on an hourly basis. Eventually, it was agreed that John and his partner would consult to them on a fee basis (as is standard in the industry), and I became John's assistant as an employee of John's firm. When the partnership later broke up, John decided to retire. My wife and I invited John and his wife to dinner and convinced him to join me in a new partnership with me providing the capital.

My father co-signed a $5,000 loan, and we worked in John's dining room for two years. In the meantime, I became a PE, and when John turned 70 years old, his wife convinced him to retire while I opened my own practice. John even gave me the drafting tables and other equipment. I called my company "Gaskell Associates Consulting Engineers," and John let me use "Formerly J.W. King Associates" in my Yellow Page advertisement.

GETTING EXPERIENCE

Once you are a graduate engineer and, hopefully, have passed the FE exam, the first step is to get a job that will give you (certifiable) experience to qualify you to eventually take the PE exam.

The Job Search

Depending on the job market at the time of your graduation, you may not have a wide range of job choices. But if you get a job designing systems for submarines, it is unlikely to lead to your own consulting engineering practice. You may have to consider commuting to a larger city to find work in your field.

First, prepare a "resume," which, at this point, will only include your education (emphasizing courses relating to consulting engineering) and your summer job, if it involved engineering. But your summer job as a life guard will not impress a prospective employer. Include praiseworthy accomplishments, like being an "Eagle Scout." Emphasize training in Computer Aided Drafting (CAD) and Building

Information Modeling (BIM), if you can, because you will be doing drafting as a major part of your job, initially. Mention interests concerning engineering, but certainly don't state an interest in eventually opening your own firm.

Get a list of consulting engineers in your area. Try to find a website for each to learn a little about them and to eliminate contractors and moon-lighters. Next, print your resume on good paper and deliver it to each engineering office on your list, don't mail it. Wear a suit and tie and explain that you are a recent (specialty) engineering graduate and would like to speak with their chief (specialty) engineer. If they ask why, reply: "I am seeking advice and will only take a few minutes." If they say he is busy, reply: "That's ok, I can wait." If all else fails, ask the receptionist to give him a copy of your resume and ask for his business card. If it is a sizable company, provide a second copy of your resume for the "Personnel Department." If you don't hear back within a week, call the engineer to verify that he received your resume and to inquire about job openings. Prepare a list of questions and have a copy ready for each call with spaces for the answers:

- Did you receive my resume?
- Are there any entry level openings?
- Are any openings likely in the near future? If so, when?
- Can you recommend competitors who might be hiring?
- Do you have any advice for a young engineer just starting out?
- Can I come in to your office and observe a typical day? (An eight hour job interview)

Send him a letter or e-mail thanking him for taking your call and for his advice. (Include another copy of your resume.)

If you don't quickly get a job, stop back to see the same people. Their needs can change in just a few weeks. Consider bringing a box of pastries or flowers for the receptionist who said that the engineer was too busy to see you.

The Interview
Be prepared:

- If you are responding to an employment posting, make a list of the skills desired so that you are prepared to discuss and relate them to your training and education. Don't be concerned if you don't have all the qualifications listed. There may be an entry-level position available.

- Make a list of five skills and qualifications of yours that you can share during the interview.
- Go to the company's website to learn more about the company so that you will be better prepared for questions, like "What interests you about our company?"
- Make a list of likely questions that you may be asked and prepare answers: Why should I hire you? Is there anything about the job or the company that I haven't told you? What are your career goals in the next 5 years and how will you achieve them? What are your salary requirements?
- Make a list of questions about the job and the company, and bring up your questions if the interviewer doesn't offer the information.
- Ask if you can meet someone in a similar position and the person who will be your immediate supervisor.
- Ask about the skills that you will be learning and applying in the available position, and access their relevance to your future goals. For example, assume that you are an electrical engineer and wish to open a practice designing electrical systems for buildings. A position as a lighting designer will not teach you the diversity of other skills needed.
- Try not to look like a "deer-in-the-headlights"; practice in front of a mirror. Listen carefully, and don't be afraid to take notes during the interview. Bring extra copies of your resume, including a list of references. Also, bring your list of questions, a pad (in a folio), and a pen. Don't bring a drink or chew gum, and turn your cell phone off.
- Send the interviewer a "Thank You" note or e-mail.

You may have to widen your job search area, but, with persistence, you will eventually get a job in your chosen field.

Start the Job Right

Once you have a job, do your best to be "exceptional." Arrive early and leave late. Start a notebook to record information, such as formulas, code rules, contacts, and anything that you might need again. Ask a lot of questions, but avoid the same question a second time—consult your "notebook."

I soon learned that Mr. King could never answer a question with a "yes" or a "no." His answers always came with a story and a long explanation. This was often frustrating when we were up-against a deadline. But it taught me related things, helped me to remember the answers, and gave me an understanding of the "why."

Fill your notebook with knowledge.

It is critically important that you stay up-to-date. This involves weekly reading, including magazines in your industry and in your specialty, code updates and interpretations, business trends, and current affairs. This will aid you in your present job and help your future engineering firm to thrive and prosper in any economy. Dedicate at least two hours a week to this task. Always have something with you to read.

White Papers

A white paper is a report or guide to help readers to understand an issue. When your work involves a new technical issue, read about it and take detailed notes in narrative form, including definitions of the various new terms.

Add this "white paper" to your notebook. I didn't learn about white papers until I was in practice for over 20 years. Start as soon as you have a job. After you have prepared a "white paper," reread it several times, and commit much of the information to memory. When the subject comes up, you will be able to discuss it like an expert. Gain a reputation as the "smartest guy in the room." White papers will serve as a useful future reference and possibly the basis of a magazine article authored by you. See more about "white papers" in Chapter 16 – Forensic Engineering.

START TO SAVE MONEY

It is important to start saving as soon as you are working unless you have a benefactor or can find a rich person to adopt you. If you are living from one pay check to the next, you will never be your own boss. If you (or your spouse) get deep into debt or ruin your credit, forget about an engineering practice. Don't live above (or up to) your means. Get as much overtime as you can, or consider a part time second job. Postpone that trip or new car until you have fulfilled your dream.

ESTABLISH RELATIONS WITH FINANCIAL INSTITUTIONS

Chapter 5 – Financial Analysis covers financing and funding needs, but you need to get an early start. If you plan to have partners, it is best for each of you to establish a relationship at different institutions. A main branch of each is usually the best choice. Also, avoid the institution that holds your mortgage to avoid the possible seizure of personal funds if your engineering practice fails.

GET KNOWN & GAIN CREDENTIALS

I was a "nobody"; I came from a blue-collar family and had never even seen the inside of a Country Club. But I was savvy enough to realize that I needed to start building an "outstanding" reputation and more credentials.

As soon as you graduate, start attending meetings of local engineering/industry organizations. Even if you don't have a job yet, it will give you an opportunity to meet fellow engineers, contractors, manufacturers' representatives, architects, inspectors, distributors, and other contacts that might help you get a job or help you in other ways.

One of the most important organizations is the local/state chapter of the National Society of Professional Engineers (NSPE). Here you will meet the "players" in the consulting engineering profession and people who will be your colleges, future competitors, or future employees. In most cases, you don't even need to join to attend meetings. Discounted memberships are offered to recent graduates, typically an 80% discount in your year of graduation. Try to get on the local mailing list so that you will be notified of meetings. They are usually evening dinner meetings with a guest speaker. Some states have many different chapters, others, like RI, only have one state chapter.

I joined several organizations and attended meetings of the following:

- *The Rhode Island Society of Professional Engineers (RISPE)*
- *Providence Engineering Society (PES)*
- *Electrical League of Rhode Island*
- *Illuminating Engineering Society of North America (IES)*

Rhode Islanders initially had to drive 50 miles to attend meetings of the Boston IES Chapter. But we had local meetings after a group of us formed the RI Chapter of the IES, of which, I'm proud to say, I was the founding president.

At meetings, collect business cards from those that you want to get to know. Start making a "Contact List" (see Chapter 9 – Marketing Materials), including both business and personal information. You will form a quicker and closer friendship if you can remember that he/she has an interest in baseball and has a 3-year-old daughter named Michelle.

Initially, my "resume" included membership in the above listed organizations. My next goal was to become a board member of RISPE. I asked the local president if there were any committee openings; there are always openings. I chose to become Publications Committee Chairman, which qualified me to attend monthly board meetings, meet the leaders, and be seen and known. Soon, I met the Nominating Committee Chairmen. After our friendship was cemented, I expressed interest in being on the board, and I became Treasurer the following year (most nominees run unopposed). That put me on the "ladder," and I became RISPE President in four years. After my presidency, I nominated one of the recent Past Presidents for the "Engineer of the Year Award"; not surprisingly, in a few years, he nominated me.

I don't mean to imply that all this was easy; it took a lot of hard work. But, with determination and effort, you can establish credentials that will eventually distinguish you from your competitors. The important lesson here is: "It doesn't just happen—you make it happen."

As a consulting engineer, you will frequently attend "interview meetings," where Building Committees select architects and engineers for their projects. I have watched many of my colleagues talk about their college degree, and then all that they had was a list of past projects. In addition, I could refer to the following:

> *I am a past President of the Rhode Island Society of Professional Engineers, the founding President of the Rhode Island Chapter of the Illuminating Engineering Society, past Director of the Electrical League of Rhode Island, and Chairman of the Electrical Code Sub-Committee of the Rhode Island Building Code Standards Committee.*
>
> *I have written numerous articles for national technical publications and have been a guest speaker at the National Conference on Harmonics and Power Quality in Philadelphia.*
>
> *I was honored by being selected "Engineer of the Year" by the Rhode Island Society of Professional Engineers and "Man of the Year" by the Electrical League of Rhode Island.*
>
> *I am particularly proud of being a recipient of the Providence Engineering Society's "Freeman Award." This award was established for the purpose of recognizing major achievements in engineering.*

I wasn't bragging; I was applying for a job.

If you want to be successful as a consulting engineer, don't be afraid to build yourself up. Fortunately, your work as an officer of professional organizations will give you many opportunities to hone your skills as a public speaker. In your consulting engineering career, you will be required to speak before both small and large groups. At this point, I am reminded of one of my least auspicious experiences as a public speaker.

During my first or second year in practice, I was hired to do a "light emissions" study. This was in conjunction with an environmental impact study relating to the proposed expansion of a local airport. I don't know if I was chosen because my resume included "Member of IES" or because I was too new to properly quote a fee for such an unusual project. In any case, I visited the airport at night, under varying weather conditions, and (with a light meter) measured the light produced from the approach lights. My final conclusion was that the amount of light was less than the light emitted by a "full moon" and, therefore, had no significant impact on the environment. I submitted my report to the environmental firm that had hired me, and it was accepted.

After about 6 months, the environmental firm called me and asked me to attend a public hearing at the City Hall to answer questions, if any. I reread my report, and, with a copy, I sat down in front with the other members of our team. The remaining 500 seats were occupied by very angry neighbors, with many more standing around the perimeter of the room. The head of the environmental firm was called to the podium and, after a few introductory remarks, said: "And now I would like to call our electrical engineer, Jack Gaskell, to the podium to present the light emissions portion of our report." I considered running for the door, but I didn't think I could make it down the center aisle.

I rose with wobbly legs and walked to the podium with my report in hand. When the heckling from the crowd quieted down a bit, I said: "I have to start out by apologizing; it was my understanding that I was here to answer questions (if any) and, therefore, did not prepare a presentation. But I have a copy of my report and will paraphrase it for you." I opened my report and stumbled through. When I was finished, everyone BOOED, and I took my seat. Even after all of these years, I still break out in a sweat when I think of that public hearing.

The lesson here is: Always be prepared to make a presentation.

OUTLINE SUMMARY

- **Plan ahead:** Don't "stumble" into becoming a consulting engineer. Plan for it.

- **Get a job:** Work at a consulting engineering practice that will qualify you to take the PE exam and give you the knowledge and experience to head-up your own firm.

- **The job search:** First, prepare a "resume" stressing CAD and BIM, if you can. Make a list of consulting engineering firms in your area and deliver your resume in person. If you don't quickly get a job, stop back to see the same people, employment needs can change quickly.

- **The interview:** Be prepared by researching the company's website. Make lists including: five skills and qualifications of yours, likely questions that you might be asked and enquires about the company. Ask if you can meet someone in a similar position and the person who will be your immediate supervisor. Send the interviewer a "Thank You" note or e-mail.

- **Start the job right:** Once you have a job, do your best to be "exceptional." Arrive early and leave late. Start a notebook to record information, such as formulas, code rules, contacts, and anything that you might need again.

- **White papers:** A white paper is a report or guide to help readers to understand an issue. When your work involves a new technical issue, read about it and take detailed notes in narrative form, including definitions of the various new terms. Add this "white paper" to your notebook.

- **Save:** Live within your means so that you will have the assets and good credit to be your own boss.

- **Banking:** Establish a relationship with a financial institution.

- **Gain credentials:** Get elected "unopposed" to Engineering Society Boards, and get nominated for prestigious awards that will distinguish you from your competitors.

- **It doesn't just happen:** "You make it happen."

PART 2
PLANNING

CHAPTER 3

START-UP OPTIONS & SPACE PLANNING

INTRODUCTION

Don't procrastinate to the point where your opportunity for your own engineering practice passes you by. Comprehend the pros and cons of each start-up option and opportunity. Find out how to evaluate offering a single discipline or multi-disciplines. Understand how you might benefit from partners and the associated pitfalls. Discover the step-by-step procedures on how to be ready when opportunity knocks.

Learn how to determine how much space your new firm will initially require and how to plan for the future growth of your firm. Gain knowledge of options, including your house, a suburban office, a downtown office, factory/industrial space, and cooperative/shared space. Discover why actually looking at spaces helps to make the right choice. Find out how easy it is to inventory and price the furniture and equipment that your office will require.

OPTIONS FOR STARTING YOUR OWN PRACTICE

When?

I like to call starting your own firm "Casting Off." I recommend that you "Cast Off" within 5 years of becoming a Professional Engineer. After that, your income and family circumstances will deter you from taking the risk. Remember that a successful practice will generate 3 to 5 times the income of that of an "employee" and will give you something valuable to sell when it comes time for retirement. But recall that there are both advantages and disadvantages, as explained in Chapter 1 – Becoming an Engineer.

Ethical Considerations

The PE Registration Laws in each state include ethical requirements. You need to be knowledgeable about these obligations in the states where you will do business and understand that these are rules and not just guidelines. Most states have a "preamble" similar to the following:

> Engineering is an important and learned profession. As members of this profession, engineers are expected to exhibit the highest standards of honesty and integrity. Engineering has a direct and vital impact on the quality of life for all people. Accordingly, the services provided by engineers require honesty, impartiality, fairness, and equity, and must be dedicated to the protection of the public health, safety, and welfare. Engineers must perform under a standard of professional behavior that requires adherence to the highest principles of ethical conduct.

In Rhode Island, they are called "Rules of Professional Conduct," and these mandates apply to both individuals and entities. They are separated into three categories: Obligations to Society, Obligations to Clients and Employer, and Obligations to other Registrants.

Depending on the state, they include items like avoiding conflicts of interest, faithfully serving the interests of your employer, not misrepresenting or exaggerating your degree of responsibility in prior assignments or in the complexity of said assignments, and not knowingly using the design, drawings, or work of another design professional.

Based on these restrictions, be sure that your new venture planning is done on your own time, carefully qualify your involvement in projects listed in your new brochure, and understand that details used by your employer (even those that you prepared) may not be yours to reuse in your new practice.

Opportunities

How to start your practice depends upon your circumstances at the time and your plans for the future. Your situation is somewhat a matter of chance, but it is also a matter of where you have positioned yourself.

In my case, Mr. King retired, leaving many loyal clients in need of a new engineer. Why not use the young guy that they had already gotten to know?

When Mr. King started his electrical career, as a teacher, he developed a funny way of talking in order to hold the attention of the class. If someone was out sick, he would say: "I hope that it was nothing trivial." He called the drawings the "Funny Papers." The specifications were the "Smellifications." Instead of opportunities, he said: "Tuneyopperties."

The following "tuneyopperties" come to mind:

- Open your practice at a time when another engineer is retiring or going out of business. You would then solicit his former clients to fill the void.
- Offer to buy a practice from a retiring engineer. He will introduce you to his clients and perhaps stay on for a short time to help you get started. A relationship like this might start as a brief partnership.
- Become a partner in an existing firm.
- Quit your job, hang out your "shingle," and start knocking on doors.

See Chapter 8 – Legal, Accounting & Insurance for more details on "Forms of Ownership."

Sole Proprietorship

I started as a "Sole Proprietor" and later became a Type "S" Corporation. Both operate similarly and are taxed on a personal basis. I liked making all the decisions without the need to get a partner's approval. The disadvantage was that I needed to come up with all the funding needs and didn't have a partner to advise against bad ideas.

Partnerships

There are pros and cons to having partners.

- **Benefits**:
  Others to share the work load (design, management, everyday tasks, and to fill-in when you're unavailable). They will also provide a portion of the start-up funds and credit and share in any losses. In addition, if the partners have different specialties, you can offer clients "multi-disciplines," "package-pricing," and "one-stop-shopping."

- **Drawbacks:**
  Others will get a portion of the profits. They will have a vote in all decisions; if you own less than a 50%, you might get out-voted. If there are just two partners, a 50/50 split is never good; someone needs to have the final say. (I know of one partnership that had a 50/50 split of the profits, but the partner that was listed second on the letterhead had 51% of the voting power.) Partners will likely have different work ethic, energy levels and personal circumstances. If additional funds are later needed, will they be willing to provide their fair share? Will their spouses let them? These are some of the factors that you will have to struggle with.

I remember during my first month working for Mr. King, I attended a new project meeting at an architectural office: a partnership of two men in their 50's. They were both likable and competent architects. But when one of them excused himself and left the room, the other bad-mouthed him. Later, the same thing happened in reverse, and I don't just mean derogatory.

"Single" Vs "Multi" Discipline

Will your firm offer a single discipline (electrical, mechanical, plumbing, fire protection, structural, or civil), or will you offer more than one specialty? A common "multi-discipline firm" is an MEPFP offering mechanical (heating, ventilating, and air conditioning), electrical, plumbing, and fire protection (sprinklers). These services require an electrical engineer and one or more mechanical engineers. If you want to be a multi-discipline firm, you could hire an employee to perform the second function. However, he would have to be a professional engineer and his seal (stamp) would have to appear on his drawings. This makes him "personally" liable for any errors or omissions, even though you own the company, are a corporation, and have professional liability insurance.

Some firms operate under these circumstances. But it is more common that the chief engineer of each discipline is an owner, regardless of the form of ownership.

I have observed the following trends. The really big engineering firms offer all disciplines. The multi-discipline firms tend to be heating, ventilating, air conditioning, electrical, plumbing, and fire protection (MEPFP). The single-discipline firms are usually structural, civil, electrical, or mechanical only. Another factor to consider is "common practice" in your geographical area of practice.

When I started practicing engineering in Rhode Island, there were two large A/E (architectural/engineering) firms with architects and engineers of all disciplines under one roof. In addition, there were many smaller architectural firms, including many sole practitioners. Some of these advertised themselves as A/E Firms, but, in fact, they had no engineers. Smaller architects would never use engineers from the large A/E Firms because these firms were their competitors. With few exceptions, the engineering firms in RI were single discipline.

Our nearest competitors were in Boston, 50 miles away. In the early 1970's, that was like being in another country. You couldn't trust those "foreigners" to show-up when there was a problem during construction.

I practiced my whole career as a consulting electrical engineer. However, it became more and more difficult as the multi-discipline firms from other states started opening branch offices in RI. Sometimes, I offered a client a "coordinated package" of services, but clients understood that the other disciplines were not "in-house." RI is too small to convince them otherwise.

Eventually, I sold my practice to a large engineering firm and stayed on to help the new division get established. My first goal was to make our division multi-discipline.

SPACE PLANNING

Space Layout

In the early stages of planning and in preparing your Business Plan, you will need to estimate the size of space that you will need for your office. You will want to estimate associated needs: furniture, equipment, and office supplies. Start by looking around the engineering office where you are currently employed. The following general spaces come to mind (add/delete, as needed):

- Reception/Waiting
- Conference
- CAD/Design Area
- Secretarial

- Printing Area
- Library
- Storage
- Break Room

In addition, mechanical equipment and restrooms may be part of your space and may need to be included in your space needs. Also, if possible, include space for expansion and unknown needs.

For the purpose of this example, let's assume you're starting a new firm with two other partners. You will be a multi-discipline firm offering electrical, HVAC, plumbing, and fire protection. In addition, you will have one full time receptionist (who will also serve as the secretary and bookkeeper) and one other part-time design/CAD person. Also, let's assume that the part-timer will eventually become full-time and one more designer/CAD person will later be added.

Next, take some sketch paper with a grid of ¼ inch = 1'-0" and rough out a sketch meeting your needs. Don't worry about walls or which space needs to be where. Just fit in everything roughly to scale. Figures **3-1** and **3-2** are the results of my effort. My area requirements measure 2,294 sq. ft. Therefore, for this example, 2,000 to 3,000 square feet of space is tentatively needed. However, keep in mind that most start-up firms need to be very cautious about adding full-time employees. So, extra space for moon-lighters (part-timers working after their day jobs) is an important consideration, and it may take two or three part-timers to offset the work of one full-time employee.

SPACE PLANNING (1 OF 2)

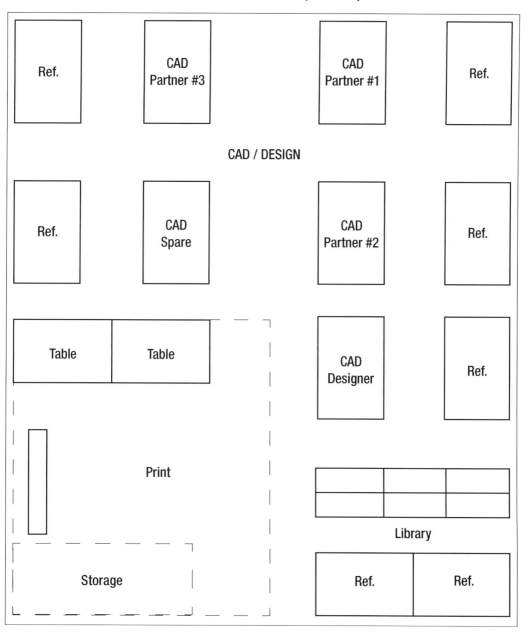

FIGURE 3-1

SPACE PLANNING (2 OF 2)

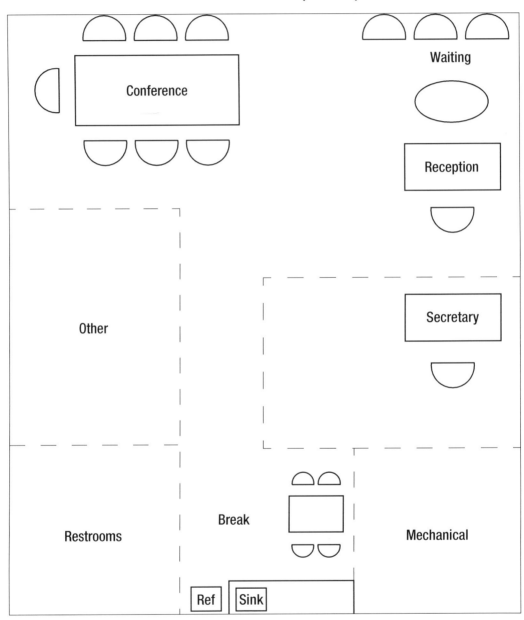

FIGURE 3-2

Rental Options

Avoid purchasing a building until you become established. Keep your cash and credit in reserve for unanticipated operating expenses and to possibly fund the addition of staff.

Consider various rental options and associated costs.

As previously discussed, I started my engineering practice when my partner, John King, retired. One of our clients was a landscape architect who had his office on the second floor of a two story office building. There were two other spaces on the second floor: a small office already rented and a two room space that was vacant. I rented this space without considering anything else and without trying to negotiate the rent. Hopefully, you will do a little more market research.

The "general" location options that come to mind are:

Your House

This is your cheapest option and is worth considering if there are no more than three of you and your budget will not support rent. But this doesn't give you a "business" presence or a suitable space for a conference or client meeting. Quietly check zoning laws. They restrict business activity in residential areas, but professional practices are usually permitted with restrictions on the number of employees and other things. If you are starting alone on a "shoe string," this may be your only option.

However, to be successful in a home based practice, you need to be "self-disciplined." You must manage your time and not allow family/personal distractions to interfere with your work duties.

After about two years at my first office location, I experienced a scary situation. The office next to mine was rented to a furniture store and was only open on Saturday mornings to collect weekly payments from the neighborhood customers. I was working one Saturday afternoon and heard someone in the hall. So, I opened my door to tell them that the furniture store office was closed. I encountered a person with a ski mask and a hand-gun. I slammed the door and hid in my second room while calling 911. I didn't even have the presence of mind to lock the door. When the police arrived, I couldn't tell them if it was a man or woman, black or white, short or tall. I couldn't even describe the pistol except to say that it was HUGE, bigger than a bread box!

Shortly thereafter, my wife and I bought a house that had a small office behind it (attached to the garage). Being separate from the house, it avoided many of the family distractions and allowed me to easily return to work after dinner. It was sufficient for a few years, but when I added a third employee, we moved to a suburban, storefront office, which improved our image. If you start out in your house, move to a real office as soon as you can afford it.

Suburban Office
This option avoids the congestion and parking problems of a downtown office and usually has much lower rental rates.

Downtown Office
If most of your clients are centered in a big city, you may need a downtown office. But you will need to budget "parking costs" for you and your employees. Instead of Class "A" space, consider "B" or "C." For start-up businesses, Class "A" and "B" are usually cost prohibitive.

Factory/Industrial
This can be an inexpensive option and may be worth considering but may have drawbacks. Will the parking/exterior and public spaces be maintained to your standards? Are heating systems/AC/Plumbing provided and available 24/7/365? Will your electric meter be powering part of your neighbor's space? Will some tenants be noisy or living in their spaces?

Cooperative/Shared
This is a relatively new concept where certain spaces and services are shared. For instance, you would have a small private space and there would be a receptionist/secretary for several professionals: engineers, attorneys, doctors, etc. Shared spaces might include reception areas, conference rooms, break rooms, rest rooms, and copy/fax rooms. As your personal space needs grow, this option soon becomes cost prohibitive.

Rent & Utilities
Investigate the rental market in your area. It is best to actually look at some available spaces. Avoid telling the rental agents that you will not actually be signing a lease agreement for another 6–8 months. Be careful in budgeting utilities; rental agents usually estimate on the low side.

Furniture & Equipment
Based on your space layout sketches, make a list of the furniture and equipment that you will need, and then go to stores (or on-line) where you actually plan to

eventually shop. Get actual prices for your Business Plan budget. Take actual measurements to be sure that everything will fit. When you actually buy, consider "going-out-of-business" sales and "used" equipment and furniture.

Keep in mind that "leasing" of furniture and equipment may be an option worth considering. This frees up capital and borrowing power, and, in many cases, there is no down payment required. Leasing agreements usually provide future purchase options at predetermined prices. Make sure that the leasing and purchasing terms are reasonable. The payments are an allowable expense. Review with your accountant beforehand.

OUTLINE SUMMARY

Options

- **Cast Off:** Within five years of becoming a registered professional engineer, start your own practice.

- **Ethics:** Carefully consider the ethical requirements of your State Boards of Registration when planning, starting, and operating your practice.

- **Start-up options:**
  - Ideally, open your practice at the time that another engineer retires.
  - Offer to buy a practice from a retiring engineer.
  - Become a partner in an existing firm.
  - Quit your job, hang out your "shingle," and start knocking on doors.

- **Sole proprietorship:** Starting as a "Sole Proprietor" is a simple option and is taxed on a personal basis. You get to make all the decisions without the need to get a partner's approval. The disadvantage is that you need to come up with all the funding needs and didn't have a partner to advise against bad ideas.

- **Partnerships:** Carefully consider the pros and cons of being on your own or having partners.
  - Pros: Partners share the workload, help with funding, share the losses, and make a multi-discipline firm more feasible.
  - Cons: Partners share in the profits and the decisions while having a different work ethic, energy levels, and commitment than you do.

- **Disciplines:** Choose which engineering specialties that your firm will offer. Common practice in your geographical area may be your deciding factor. I have observed the following trends. The really big engineering firms offer all disciplines. The multi-discipline firms tend to be heating, ventilating, air conditioning, electrical, plumbing, and fire protection (MEPFP). The single-discipline firms are usually structural, civil, electrical, or mechanical only.

Space Planning

- **Prepare a sketch:** It is not important where rooms are with respect to each other as long as each area meets your needs and is approximately to scale.

- **Office space options:** Consider various rental options and associated costs.
  - Your House: This is your cheapest option and is worth considering if there are no more than three of you and your budget will not support rent. But this doesn't give you a "business" presence or a suitable space for a conference or client meeting.
  - Suburban Office: This option avoids the congestion and parking problems of a downtown office and usually has much lower rental rates.
  - Downtown Office: If most of your clients are centered in a big city, you may need a downtown office. But you will need to budget "parking costs" for you and your employees.
  - Factory/Industrial: This can be an inexpensive option and may be worth considering but may have drawbacks: maintenance of public spaces, heating systems/AC/Plumbing and electric, neighbors noisy or living in their spaces.
  - Cooperative/Shared: A small private space and a shared receptionist/secretary, reception area, conference rooms, break rooms, rest rooms, and copy/fax rooms. As your personal space needs grow, this option soon becomes cost prohibitive.

- **Inventory:** Make a list of furniture and equipment from your sketch, and shop to get actual prices for your Business Plan and to be sure that everything will fit.

- **Used & leasing:** Consider options of used and leasing to conserve cash.

C H A P T E R   4

FINANCIAL FORECASTING

INTRODUCTION

You will discover how easy it is to estimate both your Start-Up Costs and First Year Cash Outflows and why you should update your estimate monthly and annually. Learn how to conserve cash by financing or leasing. Find out the secrets of successful firms, like including reimbursable expenses in your contracts. Comprehend why buying-in-bulk is not always the best option.

You will see that confiding in potential clients will create loyalty and a commitment to you and your new engineering practice. You will notice how identifying potential clients may be easier than you might think. Realize which people that you already know may be willing to help you. Observe how questions about upcoming projects and expressions of interest can commit these projects to you before the competition ever hears about them. Come to know how much proposed projects will generate in fees for you and when these fees will likely be received.

COSTS & CASH OUTFLOWS

Terminology

Start-Up Costs – These are the one-time costs of starting your engineering practice. From an accounting point of view, they are not expenses because they are depreciated and only a portion of these costs are allowable as an expense of the first year.

Cash Outflows – These are cash paid out. Most are operating expenses, but some of these, like loan principal payments, are classified differently from an accounting point of view.

Start-Up Costs

The following is a list of typical costs needed to get your firm started. Add/delete items as required to suit your proposed practice:

- Office Fit-out (paint, carpet, partitions, window treatments) (1)* (* Number refers to explanations later in this chapter)
- Office Furniture (2)
- Office Equipment (2)
- Computer Software (2)
- Office Phone System (2)

Cash Outflows

- Professional Salaries (PEs who are not you or your partners) (3)
- Clerical Salaries (4)
- Officer Salaries (5)
- Payroll Taxes (6)
- Payroll Services (7)
- Auto (mileage reimbursement) (8)
- Travel and Entertainment (9)
- Printing Expenses (10)
- Office Supplies (11)
- Postage and Deliveries (12)
- Dues and Subscriptions (13)
- Professional Development (seminars/training) (14)
- General Insurance (15)
- Professional Liability Insurance (16)
- Health Insurance (17)
- Rent (don't initially buy an office) (18)
- Utilities (18)
- Building Repairs and Maintenance (if not included in rent) (19)
- Equipment Repairs and Maintenance (20)
- Telephone and Internet (if not included under utilities) (21)

- Advertising for Employees (22)
- Loan Re-payments (23)
- Professional Expenses (accountant and attorney) (24)
- Office Cleaning (25)
- Miscellaneous (26)

If you didn't throw this book across the room after reading this list, I congratulate you.

Note the following in regard to the previous items:

1   Some office spaces are more "move-in ready" than others. Some landlords will pay for some fit-out work. It may be wise to start out in a low cost "factory type space" or even your basement or spare bedroom until you become established. Most meetings are at your client's office anyway. Impressing the service people and salesmen who call on you will not improve your bottom line. Having nicer digs will help when hiring employees.

2   Purchasing of furniture, equipment, a phone system, etc. can often be financed with a small down payment or leased. This will postpone part of the start-up cost until the fees start coming in. But, even if you choose any form of "corporation" as your form of business ownership, you and your partners will each have to "personally" sign an "I owe you," and you will each be jointly and severally liable, even if your business goes bankrupt. Don't forget the cost of computer software. Computer Aided Drafting (CAD) software and Building Information Modeling (BIM) software are a significant expense. Be sure that your software choices are compatible with those of your clients'. Assure that you have a license for each computer; avoid accusations from disgruntled employees of software piracy.

3   To hold down cash outflows, initially try to avoid hiring PEs who are not partners. If one of the partners doesn't have the expertise in a specialty needed, consider "farming out" that work to another consultant. Don't hire a "moon-lighter" because he won't have Professional Liability Insurance.

4   With the advent of computer programs (such as Microsoft Word and Excel), it may be unnecessary to have clerical help. If needed, consider "part-time" without benefits.

5   While preparing to form your own practice, you and your partners should have been saving. Therefore, each of you should initially get by on a salary of 80–85% of what you were paid working for someone else.

6   Your accountant will estimate payroll taxes as a percent of payroll and provide the forms.

7   Payroll has become more complicated and one of the biggest headaches of doing business. A payroll service company is relatively inexpensive; don't try to do it yourself. Review this with your CPA.

8   Avoid purchasing automobiles. Pay employees mileage instead. Your accountant can advise regarding the rate. If partners drive few work related miles, instead pay them for gas. If you can't hire an employee without providing a car, offer to reimburse their lease payments. Don't lease it for them because you will be stuck with the car and the lease if they leave.

9   Travel is for reimbursing someone for a flight, train travel, or a taxi required for business or professional purposes. Entertainment is a necessary expense. You and your senior people should be reimbursed for buying a meal or (limited) drinks for clients or potential clients.

10 If you are working for an architect, you may not be able to get reimbursed for printing unless he covers reimbursement in his contract with his client. In some cases, you can only get reimbursed if you send items out to a printer instead of printing "in-house." Check in advance, but there is not always enough time to send drawings out for printing. With today's technology, you may be able to send the printer an electronic file. For private clients, try to include printing as a reimbursable in your contract. Recently, I have seen a "print-on-demand" method used for bidding; contractors call the printer for plans and specifications and pay for printing. This is a bad idea. A contractor donates a week or more of his time preparing a bid for a job which he probably won't win. It is insulting to also make him pay for printing and

it discourages bidders. Make sure that the project owner/developer pays for printing, if you have a say.

11 Look through your present work space and the supply closet, and make a list of office supplies that you will need. Go shopping to get prices for your Business Plan. It is usually cheaper to buy office supplies in quantity, but I advise buying no more than a 3 month supply of anything. Conserve your cash. Anything in large quantities tends to disappear.

12 If you can mail it, don't deliver it unless someone is going there anyway. When leaving a regular client's office, ask if there is anything going back to your company to avoid a pick-up call. Consider a "postage meter"; stamps can also disappear.

13 In most cases, avoid country club memberships, at least until you become established. But your key people should join professional and industry organizations and attend meetings regularly, with your company picking up the tab.

14 Don't hesitate to pay for training courses when they are needed and directly relate to a person's job, lead to an engineering degree, or help advancement within your company. Train them and they might leave; don't train them and they will stay. I paid for engineering courses: 100% for A, 75% for B, and 50% for C.

15 I recommend working with a well-established, "independent" insurance agent. He can usually handle both your "general" and "professional liability" needs. See Chapter 8 – Legal, Accounting & Insurance.

16 Professional liability insurance, more commonly known as errors and omissions (E&O), is a form of liability insurance that helps protect individuals and companies when providing professional advice and service, from bearing the full cost of defending against a negligence claim made by a client, and from damages awarded in such a civil lawsuit. See Chapter 8 – Legal, Accounting & Insurance.

17 All full-time employees and their families should have health insurance. But your company can't afford it unless everyone contributes a "co-pay." You probably can't afford insurance for part-time employees, if any.

18 Your research of rental options in Chapter 3 – Start-Up Options & Space Planning will give you a good idea of rental rates and utility costs.

19 Building repairs and maintenance, if not included in your rent, are a guess. (Get out your crystal ball.)

20 Consider a contract for equipment repairs and maintenance. Even if you don't plan to purchase the contract, it will serve as a cost estimate.

21 Conversations with your proposed telephone and internet providers will reveal a monthly budget. Don't forget your cell phone provider.

22 The cost for newspaper help wanted ads and employment agencies will depend on your hiring plans. Consider internet sources; some are free.

23 Loan repayments are usually on a monthly basis. Most financial institutions require automatic withdrawal from your business checking account. If your bank does not, arrange for it to ensure that you are not late.

24 Your CPA can estimate his average monthly charges for accounting. Attorney fees will vary; make a guess for the year, and divide it into monthly payments.

25 If you are responsible for weekly cleaning, consider a janitorial service. Office cleaning should be provided by an outside firm. Don't require your staff to do it; they will resent it, especially cleaning toilets. Get proof of insurance. Having carpets frequently professionally cleaned will keep your office looking good and extend the life of the carpet. Duct cleaning will reduce absenteeism.

26 Miscellaneous is the category most scrutinized by your bank and, eventually, the IRS. Keep this as small as possible by adding other specific categories for large items.

This may seem a bit complicated, but I feel that it can be better understood by considering an example.

Example

> In this example, let's estimate the start-up costs and first year cash out-flows for the small firm described in Chapter 3 – Start-Up Options & Space Planning, including the furniture and equipment needs depicted in Figures **3-1** and **3-2.**
>
> First, I created the form shown in Figure **4-1** to break down the "start-up" costs. Next, I completed this form by including the costs for my example firm, thus creating Figure **4-2**. (Note that you can download all of these forms from my website at no charge.)
>
> Then, I created the form shown in Figure **4-3** from the categories listed above to include the totals of each category of expense for each month, the total of all expenses for each month, the total of each category of expense for the year, and the grand total of all expenses for the year.
>
> Lastly, I completed this form by including both the start-up costs and the operating cash outflows for my example firm, thus creating Figure **4-4.**

Modify these forms to suit your proposed firm. Resist the temptation to pro-portion these costs/outflows to your situation; include current pricing applicable to your geographical area. Once in operation, update them monthly and compare changes to your original estimate. This will help to keep your budgeting current and to avoid surprises. Continue to do so each year.

START-UP COSTS

#	EXPENSE ITEMS	EACH	ITEM	SUB TOTALS
Office Fit-Out				
LS	Paint			
LS	Carpet			
LS	Window Treatments			
LS	Break Room Preparation			
	Sub Total (Fit-Out)			
Office Furniture				
4	CAD Furniture			
8	Reference Tables			
12	Book Cases			
16	Chairs			
1	Table (Conference Room)			
1	Table (Waiting Room)			
1	Table (Break Room)			
2	Desks			
8	File Cabinets			
	Sub Total (Office Furniture)			
Equipment				
1	Blueprint Machine			
1	Refrigerator			
1	Copy/Fax machine			
4	CAD Computers and Software			
2	Laptop Computers and Software			
5	Printers			
1	Power Point Projector			
	Sub Total (Equipment)			
Office Phone System				
LS	Equipment			
LS	Instillation			
	Sub Total Phone System			
Other				
	Sub Total Other			
TOTAL START-UP EXPENSES				

FIGURE 4-1

START-UP COSTS EXAMPLE

#	EXPENSE ITEMS	EACH	ITEM	SUB TOTALS
Office Fit-Out				
LS	Paint		1,500	
LS	Carpet		5,000	
LS	Window Treatments		1,500	
LS	Break Room Preparation		2,000	
	Sub Total (Fit-Out)			10,000
Office Furniture				
4	CAD Furniture	300	1,200	
8	Reference Tables	100	800	
12	Book Cases	70	840	
16	Chairs	150	2,400	
1	Table (Conference Room)	300	300	
1	Table (Waiting Room)	200	200	
1	Table (Break Room)	150	150	
2	Desks	300	600	
8	File Cabinets	220	1,760	
	Sub Total (Office Furniture)			8,250
Equipment				
1	Blueprint Machine	4,000	4,000	
1	Refrigerator	200	200	
1	Copy/Fax machine	500	500	
4	CAD Computers and Software	3,150	12,600	
2	Laptop Computers and Software	1,250	2,500	
5	Printers	200	1,000	
1	Power Point Projector	700	700	
	Sub Total (Equipment)			21,500
Office Phone System				
LS	Equipment		1,500	
LS	Instillation		1,000	
	Sub Total Phone System			2,500
Other				
	Sub Total Other			0
TOTAL START-UP EXPENSES				$42,250

FIGURE 4-2

FIRST YEAR CASH OUTFLOWS

EXPENSE	ANNUAL	JAN.	FEB.	MARCH	APRIL	MAY	JUNE	JULY	AUG.	SEPT.	OCT.	NOV.	DEC.
Office Fit-out													
Office Furniture													
Office Equipment													
Software & Up-dates													
Office Phone System													
Professional Salaries													
Clerical Salaries													
Officers Salaries													
Payroll Taxes													
Payroll Services													
Auto													
Travel & Entertainment													
Bluprint Expense													
Office Supplies													
Postage & Delivery													
Dues & Subscriptions													
Professional Development													
General Insurance													
Professional Liability Ins.													
Health Insurance													
Rent													
Utilities													
Bld. Repairs & Maint.													
Equip. Repairs & Maint.													
Telephone & Internet													
Employment Ads.													
Loan Re-payments													
Professional Expenses													
Office Cleaning													
Miscellaneous													
TOTALS													

FIGURE 4-3

FIRST YEAR CASH OUTFLOWS EXAMPLE

EXPENSE	ANNUAL	JAN.	FEB.	MARCH	APRIL	MAY	JUNE	JULY	AUG.	SEPT.	OCT.	NOV.	DEC.
Office Fit-out	$10,000	$10,000											
Office Furniture	$8,250	$8,250											
Office Equipment	$18,000	$18,000											
Software & Up-dates	$3,500	$3,500											
Office Phone System	$2,500	$2,500											
Professional Salaries	$104,000	$4,333	$4,333	$4,333	$4,333	$4,333	$4,333	$13,000	$13,000	$13,000	$13,000	$13,000	$13,002
Clerical Salaries	$52,000	$4,333	$4,333	$4,333	$4,333	$4,333	$4,333	$4,333	$4,333	$4,333	$4,333	$4,333	$4,337
Officers Salaries	$240,000	$20,000	$20,000	$20,000	$20,000	$20,000	$20,000	$20,000	$20,000	$20,000	$20,000	$20,000	$20,000
Payroll Taxes	$47,520	$3,440	$3,440	$3,440	$3,440	$3,440	$3,440	$4,480	$4,480	$4,480	$4,480	$4,480	$4,481
Payroll Services	$2,400	$200	$200	$200	$200	$200	$200	$200	$200	$200	$200	$200	$200
Auto	$5,000	$416	$416	$416	$416	$416	$416	$416	$416	$416	$416	$416	$424
Travel & Entertainment	$5,000	$416	$416	$416	$416	$416	$416	$416	$416	$416	$416	$416	$424
Bluprint Expense	$2,500	$208	$208	$208	$208	$208	$208	$208	$208	$208	$208	$208	$212
Office Supplies	$11,000	$5,500			$1,833				$1,833			$1,834	
Postage & Delivery	$3,000	$250	$250	$250	$250	$250	$250	$250	$250	$250	$250	$250	$250
Dues & Subscriptions	$2,000	$166	$166	$166	$166	$166	$166	$166	$166	$166	$166	$166	$174
Professional Development	$2,000	$166	$166	$166	$166	$166	$166	$166	$166	$166	$166	$166	$174
General Insurance	$3,000	$250	$250	$250	$250	$250	$250	$250	$250	$250	$250	$250	$250
Professional Liability Ins.	$10,000	$833	$833	$833	$833	$833	$833	$833	$833	$833	$833	$833	$837
Health Insurance	$19,000	$1,404	$1,404	$1,404	$1,404	$1,404	$1,404	$1,762	$1,762	$1,762	$1,762	$1,762	$1,766
Rent	$31,408	$4,832	$2,416	$2,416	$2,416	$2,416	$2,416	$2,416	$2,416	$2,416	$2,416	$2,416	$2,416
Utilities	$4,000	$333	$333	$333	$333	$333	$333	$333	$333	$333	$333	$333	$337
Bld. Repairs & Maint.	$2,500	$208	$208	$208	$208	$208	$208	$208	$208	$208	$208	$208	$212
Equip. Repairs & Maint.	$2,000	$166	$166	$166	$166	$166	$166	$166	$166	$166	$166	$166	$174
Telephone & Internet	$10,000	$833	$833	$833	$833	$833	$833	$833	$833	$833	$833	$833	$837
Employment Ads.	$500						$250	$250					
Loan Re-payments	$48,000	$4,000	$4,000	$4,000	$4,000	$4,000	$4,000	$4,000	$4,000	$4,000	$4,000	$4,000	$4,000
Professional Expenses	$6,000	$500	$500	$500	$500	$500	$500	$500	$500	$500	$500	$500	$500
Office Cleaning	$3,800	$300	$300	$300	$300	$300	$500	$300	$300	$300	$300	$300	$300
Miscellaneous	$20,000	$2,500	$1,590	$1,590	$1,590	$1,590	$1,590	$1,590	$1,590	$1,590	$1,590	$1,590	$1,600
TOTALS	$678,878	$97,837	$46,761	$46,761	$48,594	$46,761	$47,211	$57,076	$58,659	$56,826	$56,826	$58,660	$56,907

FIGURE 4-4

CASH INFLOWS

Terminology

Cash Inflows – I have used the term "Cash Inflows" instead of "Income" to coincide with the term "Cash Outflows" used earlier in this chapter.

Clients

First, make a list of your proposed clients. If you need to expand your list, consider seeking referrals from your contact list, consultants of a different specialty, land surveyors, and contractors in your specialty. Other potential clients are found in the yellow pages, on the internet, and in newspapers.

Try to meet with potential clients privately at their office or over lunch at a quiet restaurant. Later, prepare a spread sheet to be included as one of your supplemental materials in your Business Plan. Evaluate their level of commitment: all of their work, most of their work, __% of their work, unsure, or none. (Don't include those who say "none" in your Business Plan.)

Tell your potential clients that you are making a projection required by your bank. This will help to get their cooperation and, more importantly, their commitment. But a word of caution here: don't say anything to anyone to imply that you're uncertain about being in your own private practice—you are just complying with your bank's usual/periodic request. Above all, make it very clear that this discussion is "CONFIDENTIAL," that you have not yet given notice at your present place of employment, and that it is very important that they keep this information "private." This would also be a good time to ask for referrals, anyone else who might want to engage your services. Also, see Chapter 10 – Marketing Methods.

Fee Projections

At the same time, make a list of anticipated projects from each client over your first 12 months in business, including estimated fees and start dates. This verbally commits the client to specific projects for you. This is FANTASTIC marketing strategy disguised as information needed by your bank. Actually, the answers to most of these questions will be unknown, but record what you can. If the client has a $5M high school starting construction documents in November, I will show you in Chapter 12 – Fee Proposals how to estimate your fee and the associated cash flow. Complete a spread sheet of this data using "unknown" for names of some projects, but estimate fees for each and (based on start dates) the amount of revenue anticipated each month. Monthly cash inflow is difficult to predict. One factor is that some architects only bill at the completion of a phase. So, there may be several months without any payment on a project.

On average, it took me 60 to 90 days to receive payments, and I was aggressive at pursuing payment. (I have been told that the average is between 110 and 120 days.) I would often say: "My accountant is really pressuring me. Can I pick up a check on Friday?" (No one ever pointed out that I owned my company and the accountant was retained by me). Other times I would say: "My bank is requesting that I provide an income projection for them" or "I have a note due on Friday; can I pick-up a check tomorrow?" I always billed monthly based on my estimate of the percent complete of the project phase on which we were currently working. (See Chapter 11 – Project Phases.) However, some clients only bill when a phase is complete or "when they get around to it." I recommend calling the "slow billers" a few days before the end of the month to verify the correct percent and to pressure them to actually bill their client that month.

Create a spread sheet similar to Figure **4-5** FIRST YEAR CASH INFLOW. You will, most likely, need a "crystal ball" for these projections, but try to be realistic because your go/no go/wait decision will be based, to a great extent, on this information. After you have made a "go" decision, redo your projections with a more optimistic view before submitting your Business Plan for financing.

I strongly advise you to redo this process each year and project the next year's income. December is usually a good month to meet with clients because people are in a generous mood. Start out by thanking the clients for their past work. This process will hopefully commit your clients to certain projects for you in the future. It will also be an economic barometer for the next year. If the outlook is pessimistic, it will prompt you to start aggressive marketing and give you the opportunity to say: "How can I win more of your projects next year?" Don't forget to bring a list of current projects with you and to verify the status of each with your project manager beforehand. There is no point in lobbying for more work if there are unresolved issues on your current projects.

Example

Continuing the example (per Chapter 3), I filled out the cash inflow information in (blank) Figure **4-5**, thus creating Figure **4-6**. The result is a "hypothetical" first year cash inflow projection for fees to be received. Allow 2–4 months after billing to actually receive this income. Again, resist the temptation to proportion these estimates to your situation.

FIRST YEAR CASH INFLOWS

FIGURE 4-5

FIRST YEAR CASH INFLOWS EXAMPLE

CLIENT	PROJECT	TOT. REC.	JAN.	FEB.	MARCH	APRIL	MAY	JUNE	JULY	AUG.	SEPT.	OCT.	NOV.	DEC.
A	Office Building	32,000			3,000	3,000	3,000	3,000	3,000	3,000	3,000	3,000	3,000	5,000
	Elem. School	72,000				8,000	8,000	8,000	8,000	8,000	8,000	8,000	8,000	8,000
	Generator Study	12,000						3,000	9,000					
B	Baseball Field	20,000				4,000	5,000	5,000		3,000		3,000		
	Riverfront Park	15,000						4,000	2,000	2,000	2,000	2,000	2,000	1,000
	Unknown	25,000					5,000		5,000	5,000	5,000	5,000		
C	High School Stdy.	15,000					4,000	10,000	1,000					
	Unknown	60,000							10,000	10,000	10,000	10,000	10,000	10,000
D	Unknown	85,000							10,000	15,000	15,000	15,000	15,000	15,000
	Unknown	20,000									20,000			
	Unknown	25,000								15,000				10,000
E	Library	23,000									11,000	2,000		10,000
	Dormitory	24,000						9,000				5,000	5,000	5,000
	Unknown	30,000										10,000	10,000	10,000
	Unknown	25,000							10,000			10,000	5,000	
F	Hotel Addition	19,500			7,000							5,000	2,500	5,000
	Motel	32,000					8,000	8,000	8,000	8,000				
	Unknown	10,000											10,000	
	Retail Store	6,000											3,000	3,000
G	Fire Alarm	4,500											1,500	3,000
	GInerator	5,000											5,000	
	TOTALS	560,000	0	0	10,000	15,000	33,000	50,000	66,000	69,000	74,000	78,000	80,000	85,000

FIGURE 4-6

OUTLINE SUMMARY

- **Get started**: Use the list of typical costs/outflows. Add/delete items as required to suit your practice.

- **Use two categories:** Divide into "start-up" (onetime) costs and "operating" (monthly) outflows.

- **Conserve cash:** Consider "financing" of furniture and equipment and making monthly payments for things like insurance.

- **Reimbursable:** Don't forget to bill for "reimbursable" expenses like printing, if possible.

- **Limit quantities:** Don't stock large quantities of office supplies.

- **Create & update:** Create a spreadsheet for annual and monthly cash outflows. Update it monthly, and compare changes to your original estimate. Continue to do this each year.

- **Potential clients:** Meet with each likely, potential client, and try to gauge their level of commitment to you for future work.

- **Referrals:** Seek referrals from your contact list, consultants of a different specialty, land surveyors, and contractors in your specialty.

- **Other potential clients:** Review newspapers and search on the internet.

- **Confidentiality:** Unless you have already given notice at your present place of employment, inquiries should be discreet.

- **Make projections:** Ask about projects expected within the next year and their anticipated schedule. Also, try to realistically estimate others.

- **Estimate probable fees:** (See Chapter 12 – Fee Proposals)

CHAPTER 5

FINANCIAL ANALYSIS

INTRODUCTION

Discover why your Cash Flow Analysis and Balance Sheets are your most important financial barometers. Learn how to prepare them and when to update them.

You won't be able to borrow without a cash down payment; understand what is expected. Find out which banking relationships to pursue and who has the greater "approval authority." Become aware of "due diligence" and the role that the SBA plays in the loan process. Be prepared for your meeting with the loan officer, and understand the meanings of security, guarantor, endorser, co-signer, demand note, and receivables financing.

CASH FLOW ANALYSIS

The Cash Flow Analysis that I am proposing in this chapter is somewhat of an informal way of estimating your "cash on hand" at the end of each month.

It ignores the issues like depreciation, capital expense determination, etc. Your CPA will take care of these things when he does your year-end accounting. You need to do a Cash Flow Analysis for your initial Business Plan, your subsequent yearly Business Plan, and for each month that you are in business.

Prepare a final spreadsheet combining the Cash Inflows and Cash Outflows into a projected cash flow. See Figure **5-1** Cash Flow Analysis

Capital Contribution

This is the cash that you and your partners are putting into the business. It may come from your savings, a gift, or a refinancing of your home.

Bank Loans

Start out with a guess. As you do your Cash Flow Analysis, if your cash on hand at the end of any month gets too low, you either need to put up more capital or get a larger loan.

Cash Inflows

These are the amounts that I included in Figure **4-6**.

Cash Outflows

These are the amounts that I included in Figure **4-4.**

Cash On Hand

This is your anticipated available cash. It may be all in your checking account or part of it may be in a savings account in the name of your business.

Include your First Year Cash Flow Analysis in your Business Plan. (See Chapter 6 – Business Plan.) After you actually start your business, keep a record of each month's activity and use it to help you in forecasting next year's Cash Flow Projections.

Example – Cash Flow Analysis

Continuing the example (per Chapters 3 and 4), I filled in both the Cash Inflow and Start-Up Cost information in (blank) Figure **5-1**, thus creating Figure **5-2**. The result is a "hypothetical" first year cash flow projection. Again, resist the temptation to proportion these estimates to your situation.

CASH FLOW ANALYSIS

ITEM	JAN.	FEB.	MAR.	APR.	MAY.	JUN.	JLY.	AUG.	SEP.	OCT.	NOV.	DEC.
Capital Contribution												
Bank Loan												
Add-Cash inflows												
Less-Cash outflows												
Cash on hand												

FIGURE 5-1

CASH FLOW ANALYSIS EXAMPLE

ITEM	JAN.	FEB.	MAR.	APR.	MAY.	JUN.	JLY.	AUG.	SEP.	OCT.	NOV.	DEC.
Capital Contribution	100,000											
Bank Loan	200,000											
Add-Cash inflows	0	0	10,000	15,000	33,000	50,000	66,000	69,000	74,000	78,000	80,000	85,000
Less-Cash outflows	97,837	46,761	46,761	48,594	46,761	47,211	57,076	58,659	56,826	56,826	58,660	56,907
Cash on hand	202,163	155,402	118,641	85,047	71,286	74,075	82,999	93,340	110,514	131,688	153,028	181,121

FIGURE 5-2

BALANCE SHEETS

The final thing that you need is a "balance sheet" for the start of your practice (opening) and for the end of your first year (closing). Hopefully, "closing" means the closing of your books for your first successful year, not the closing of the doors. See Figure **5-3** Balance Sheet.

Example – Balance Sheets

I combined the results of **4-4**, **4-6**, and **5-2** into blank form **5-3** to create **5-4** Balance Sheet – Example.

Most of the entries are self-explanatory.

Current Liabilities – Bank Loans Payable (1 year)

This is "principal payments" on the bank loan for the coming year.

Current Assets – Accounts Receivable

The opening balance is, of course, zero because there is nothing to bill yet. The amount at the end of the first year is more complicated. The cash inflows in **4-6** are projections of the "actual" amounts received each month. The accounts receivable are the billings delayed by 60–120 days. You could estimate the accounts receivable at the end of the first year by redoing **4-6,** assuming cash was received when billed. Then, redo **5-2**. The difference between the "cash on hand" on the two forms, **4-6** and **5-2,** at the end of December is the receivables. As an alternative, you could just guess like I did. The only important thing is that you are projecting a positive cash flow for the entire year. Trust me, receivables are always substantial.

Current Assets – Pre-paid

Usually, your landlord will require the last month's rent in advance and, often, taxes are pre-paid.

Fixed Assets – Accumulated Depreciation

Tell your CPA how much you project for start-up costs, and he will provide the depreciation estimate.

Current Liabilities – Accounts Payable & Other Liabilities

These are items usually found on a balance sheet. Include a guess here to show that you did not overlook these items.

BALANCE SHEET

ASSETS	OPENING - January 1st	CLOSING - December 31st
Current Assets		
Cash (Partner Contributions)		
Cash (Bank Loan)		
Cash on hand		
Accounts Receivable		
Prepaid Expenses		
Total Current Assets		
Fixed Assets		
Furniture & Equipment		
Leasehold improvements		
Less - Accumulated Depreciation		
Total Fixed Assets		
TOTAL ASSETS		
LIABILITIES		
Current Liabilities		
Bank Loan Payable (1 year)		
Accounts Payable		
Accrued Expenses		
Total Current Liabilities		
Long-term Debt		
Bank Loan Payable (beyond 1 year)		
TOTAL LIABILITIES		
CAPITAL		
Partners Loans (Owners starting equity)		
Net income (loss)		
Total Capital		
TOTAL LIABILITIES & CAPITAL		

FIGURE 5-3

BALANCE SHEET EXAMPLE

ASSETS	OPENING - January 1st		CLOSING - December 31st	
Current Assets				
Cash (Partner Contributions)	100,000		0	
Cash (Bank Loan)	200,000		0	
Cash on hand	0		137,042	
Accounts Receivable	0		113,000	
Prepaid Expenses	0		2,374	
Total Current Assets		300,000		252,416
Fixed Assets				
Furniture & Equipment	0		32,250	
Leasehold improvements	0		10,000	
Less - Accumulated Depreciation	0		(4,600)	
Total Fixed Assets		0		37,650
TOTAL ASSETS		300,000		290,066
LIABILITIES				
Current Liabilities				
Bank Loan Payable (1 year)	32,000		37,000	
Accounts Payable	0		25,000	
Accrued Expenses	0		5,000	
Total Current Liabilities		32,000		67,000
Long-term Debt				
Bank Loan Payable (beyond 1 year)		168,000		131,000
TOTAL LIABILITIES		200,000		198,000
CAPITAL				
Partners Loans (Owners starting equity)	100,000		100,000	
Net income (loss)	0		(7,934)	
Total Capital		100,000		92,066
TOTAL LIABILITIES & CAPITAL		300,000		290,066

FIGURE 5-4

INITIAL FUNDING NEEDS

Upon completion of your "Cash Flow Analysis," you have a pretty good guess as to your first year's funding needs. If you have followed my recommendations, this should be a realistic projection. But you need to add a safety factor. Assume that you will need more funding than projected, 20–30% more. I recommend that you include this as an identified item in your Business Plan. It shows that you are being conservative and recognize that "Cash Flow Analysis" is not an exacting science.

TYPES OF FUNDING

There are two types of funding: equity and debt.

Equity

This is what you and your partners have saved and are willing to invest in the business. Lenders will expect at least 30% of your first year funding needs to be "equity" funded.

Debt

This is borrowed money that must be paid back. Normally, the principal and interest is paid back in fixed monthly payments. Be sure that you have estimated these payments in your "Cash Flow Analysis."

EQUITY FUNDING

Gifts

Don't overlook the obvious: parents, in-laws, and close relatives. They are often willing and able to fund a professional practice that is intended to support you and your family into retirement. There should not be a written obligation to repay these funds or it will be considered "debt" funding.

Savings

Besides passbook savings accounts, "savings" include CDs, stocks, and bonds. Avoid the temptation to cash these in and deposit the proceeds into your business accounts. In most cases, there is little hassle in borrowing the cash value without the lending institution requiring your accounts as collateral.

Homeowner Second Mortgage

I realize that the term "second mortgage" will be scary to both you and your spouse. But your home equity is probably the largest portion of your net worth. In the worst case (your business fails), this gives you long-term, low interest financing of your obligation. Depending on mortgage interest rates, it may be better to refinance your home mortgage.

A big advantage of funding your new engineering practice through a mortgage is tax deductibility of interest.

Credit Cards

I don't recommend this option, but some businesses are funded by credit card debt. If each card is used regularly and the balance is paid punctually, the credit limit keeps going up. Over time, it is easy to accumulate several cards. The downside is that interest rates are higher than other types of financing, but usually not outrageous, if you choose the right cards and pay the minimum on time. But if you haven't saved and can't wangle a gift, this may be your only option. Avoid this if at all possible.

Venture Capitalists, Silent Partners & Angel Investors

If you are a medium or large start-up, you might attract funds from these sources. However, they will expect a share of equity in your company. Often, they are not paid back on a regular schedule, but they are paid upon the sale of your company. If you are in it for the long haul, this is probably not a good choice. If you are a small start-up, venture capitalists are unlikely to be interested. Also, they are not very "silent" if they disagree with management decisions. Also, some states forbid ownership in A&E firms by those who are not members of the profession.

Crowdfunding

With the passage of the JOBS Act of 2012, a new method of funding a commercial project was born. It is known as "Crowdfunding." The legislation mandates that a funding portal (platform) be used and that the portal must be registered with the SEC as well as an applicable self-regulatory organization.

Crowdfunding has its origins in the concept of crowdsourcing, which is the broader concept of an individual reaching a goal by receiving and leveraging small contributions from many parties.

Crowdfunding models include the people or organizations that propose the ideas and/or projects to be funded, the crowd of people who support the proposals, and the funding portal.

The JOBS Act places limits on the value of securities an issuer may offer and individuals can invest through crowdfunding intermediaries. An issuer may sell up to $1,000,000 of its securities per 12 months, and, depending upon their net worth and income, investors will be permitted to invest up to $100,000 in crowdfunding issues per 12 months.

This method of equity funding is too new for me to properly evaluate at the time of this writing. However, it may be worth investigating.

DEBT FUNDING

Banks
A bank is a financial institution that accepts deposits and channels those deposits into lending activities.

Savings Bank
A Savings Bank is a financial institution whose primary purpose is accepting saving deposits and paying interest on those deposits. Since deregulation in the 1980s, they offer services competitive with many commercial banks.

S&L (Savings & Loan or Thrifts)
An S&L is a financial institution that accepts savings deposits and makes mortgage and other loans but cannot have more than 20% of their lending in commercial loans. An S&L may have too many commercial loans at the time that you apply.

Credit Unions
A Credit Union is a member-owned financial cooperative operated for the purpose of promoting thrift and providing credit to its members at competitive rates.

Approval Authority
In opening your account at any financial institution, be aware that a local branch manager has less "approval authority" without the need for committee approval than does a senior manager at the main office.

SBA BUSINESS LOANS

The Small Business Administration (SBA) program is designed for business owners who may have trouble qualifying for traditional bank loans. The SBA does not give loans; it guarantees a portion of loans. Loans come from banks and other approved lenders who make the final decisions. Also, the SBA does not offer grants to start or grow a business. The SBA offers the following programs:

7(a) Loan Program

This is the SBA's primary business loan program. The standard program has a requirement of $2 million minimum in average sales, so it is probably not for you. But they have special programs, including the SBA *Express*. It provides 50% guarantee on smaller loans up to $350,000. Loans up to $25,000 do not require collateral. Maturities are usually 5 to 7 years for working capital and up to 25 years for real estate or equipment. Revolving lines of credit are allowed for a maximum of 7 years. Applicant must demonstrate that credit is otherwise not available. Other special programs include the *Patriot Express* for veterans.

Microloan Program

This SBA program provides small loans ranging from $500 to $50,000 to women, low income, minority, veterans, and other small businesses owners through non-profit intermediaries. The maximum term for a microloan is 7 years.

Small Business Investment Company Program

This program fills the gap between what owners can fund directly and their needs for growth. The SBICs are privately owned investment funds.

Each of these programs is subject to change, and new programs become available from time to time. For more information, visit: www.sba.gov.

EVALUATIONS BY FUNDING SOURCES

If you have saved all that you need to start your consulting engineering practice, I congratulate you as one of the few. If you inherited wealth or won the lottery, I envy you. But if you are like most of us, you are going to need funding. The financial institution that you go to is required to do what is called "due diligence" and will require the following:

- A neatly bound copy of your "Business Plan." (See Chapter 6.)
- "Your Net-Worth Statement," which lists your assets and liabilities. It is important that it is not negative and that you have some liquid assets, like savings and investments (in addition to 401Ks and IRAs), and don't have credit card debt that is not paid off monthly. Each partner will have to provide this information.
- Know your "credit rating" and be prepared to discuss it.
- In addition, expect that a "credit check" will be done regarding each of you.
- Also, in most cases, a "background check" will be done.
- It is also common, nowadays, to do a "social media check."

It is important that you <u>prepare</u> for the meeting with the loan officer. This is one of the most important meetings of your life, but if you are prepared, you will make a great impression. Not only will the bank be evaluating your business plan, but it will also be judging your presentation as it relates to your ability to win clients and projects.

- Dress professionally. Try to appear self-confident, enthusiastic, and well-informed.
- Prepare a 20 minute presentation of your business plan. Assume that the loan officer does not know what type of engineering that your firm does or even what a consulting engineer ensures. Sound professional, but remember that you are talking to a "layperson." Don't talk down to the loan officer.
- Stress your ability to service the debt, your level of commitment, and your integrity as demonstrated by your credit history.
- Thank the loan officer for his time and consideration. A "thank you" note or e-mail is always a good idea.

LOAN SECURITY

Lenders will not give you a loan unless they are convinced that your business will be successful and there is a strong likelihood that the loan will be repaid. Nevertheless, they want to be covered in case of default.

Often a "personal guarantee commitment" is all that is required. Don't offer more than is necessary. If they ask for more, enquire: "Is that really required?" It may be worth your while to shop around to other financial institutions regarding this issue.

Guarantor

For new businesses, lenders will usually expect you and all of your partners to sign a personal guarantee commitment, even if you are a corporation. This makes you each jointly and severable liable for the loan (meaning you are each "individually" liable for the "full" amount). Try to negotiate a limited guarantee to cover the shortfall if other securities have been pledged.

Endorser

This makes someone else contingently liable for the loan if you default.

Co-Signer

A co-signer is someone who agrees to be jointly liable for the loan.

Promissory Note

A promissory note is usual and includes the principal amount, interest rate, terms of payment, and the maturity date.

Demand Note

A demand note is a written promise to pay the outstanding balance upon demand. Avoid this kind of loan. Suggest a "promissory note" instead.

Mortgage

A lender may require a mortgage against your property as collateral: real estate, car, boat, etc.

Pledge of Stocks or Bonds

The lender will usually consider 50–75% of the value as security, and additional security may be required if the value of these assets declines.

IF THE LOAN IS TURNED DOWN

If your loan is turned down, try to find out why. This may give you the opportunity to correct the problem and reapply. Also, it would be helpful to know what to correct before applying elsewhere. Reasons for rejection include: insufficient collateral, lack of financial commitment on your part, a poor business plan, and your character, stability, or personality. On the other hand, the problem may be internal to the bank; perhaps they have exceeded their quota of commercial loans for the time period.

LONGTIME FUNDING NEEDS

As time goes by, you will probably need funds due to your clients being slow in paying you. This type of loan is called "Receivables Financing" or a "Line of Credit." You will have to assign your receivables to the lender to secure the loan or line of credit. Lenders may lend or extend credit on between 50% and 75% of receivables, excluding those over 90 days. Also, you will usually be required to submit a list of "aged receivables" each month.

Keep in touch with your loan officers, and be sure to include them on your mailing list.

OUTLINE SUMMARY

- **Cash flow analysis**: Estimate your "cash on hand" at the end of each month by preparing a cash flow analysis. You need it for your initial Business Plan, your subsequent yearly Business Plan, and for each month that you are in business.

- **Balance sheet:** The final thing that you need for your Business Plan is a "balance sheet" for the start of your practice (opening) and for the end of your first year (closing). Your balance sheet is your projection of how you expect your firm to grow financially for your first year and will be your key to financing. Hopefully, when you redo it using actual results, you will have exceeded expectations.

- **Buffer:** Assume that you will need more funding than projected, 20–30% more. I recommend that you include this as an identified item in your Business Plan. It shows that you are being conservative and recognize that "Cash Flow Analysis" is not an exacting science.

- **Equity funding:** Lenders will expect at least 30% of your first year funding needs to be "equity" funded.
  - Gifts: Don't overlook the obvious: parents, in-laws, and close relatives.
  - Savings: Passbook savings accounts, CDs, stocks and bonds.
  - Second Mortgage: Long-term, low interest, financing with tax deductible interest.
  - Credit Card: Possible but not recommended.
  - Venture Capitalists, Silent Partners & Angel Investors: Unlikely with pitfalls.
  - Crowdfunding: New but may be worth investigating.

- **Form multiple banking relationships:** I recommend establishing relations with two financial institutions: one should be a credit union and the other should be either a commercial bank or a savings bank.

- **Lending authority:** A local branch manager has less "approval authority" than does a senior manager at the main office.

- **SBA:** The SBA does not give loans; it guarantees a portion of loans. Also, it does not offer grants to start or grow a business. For more information, visit: www.sba.gov.

- **Due diligence:** The financial institution that you go to is required to perform what is called "due diligence" and will require much documentation from you.

- **Be prepared:** It is important that you prepare for your meeting with the loan officer.
  - Bring your Business Plan and Net-Worth Statement.
  - Be prepared to discuss your credit rating, background and social media postings.
  - Dress Professionally.
  - Be prepared to present a 20 minute presentation of your Business Plan.
  - Thank the loan officer for his time and consideration.
  - A "thank you" note or e-mail is always a good idea.

- **Security:** Lenders will want some type of security for their loan. Possibilities include guarantor, endorser, co-signer, demand note, or mortgage.

- **Receivables financing:** Funds are often needed to fund operations while waiting for your clients to pay.

CHAPTER 6

BUSINESS PLAN

INTRODUCTION

You will understand what a Business Plan includes, how you can build one, and how important it will be to the success of your engineering practice. Discover how your business plan defines your company and its goals, gives you a game plan, and helps you make a go/no go/or wait decision. Find out why updating your business plan both monthly and annually allows you to adjust expectations and/ or modify actions to compensate. Ascertain how the selection of your company name affects both how it identifies you and the future salability of your practice. Observe that your business plan will be the "key tool" in seeking financing and a line of credit, both for start-up and for cash flow needs.

WRITE A BUSINESS PLAN

This is one of the most important and frequently overlooked steps in the process of starting your own engineering practice. *When I started my practice, I didn't even know what a business plan was. That is probably why I "stumbled" along by the seat of my pants and succeeded by luck and perseverance.*

WHY IS A BUSINESS PLAN IMPORTANT?

- It is the "structure" of your practice which precisely defines your company and identifies your goals.

- It will organize your thoughts and will give you a "game plan."
- It will help you make a "go/no go/or wait" decision.
- It will help you in forecasting funding needs and securing "financing."

It is critically important that you have patience and take the time to properly research and thoughtfully write a clear and concise document. It will be necessary to update this business "guide" annually.

During your first year in business, you will find it helpful to compare projections to actual cash flows on a monthly basis, to adjust expectations accordingly, or to modify actions to compensate.

WHAT DOES A BUSINESS PLAN INCLUDE?

- Cover Page
- Table of Contents
- Executive Summary
- Business Description
- My Qualifications (or "The Management Team")
- Ownership Agreement (if not a Sole Proprietor)
- Operations Plan
- Legal, Records/Taxes & Insurance

- Marketing Plans
- Start-Up Costs
- Cash Outflow Projections
- Cash Inflow Projections
- Cash Flow Analysis
- Balance Sheets
- Financing Overview & Funding Needs
- Supplemental Materials

Cover Page

Basically, this should include your proposed firm name, the words BUSINESS PLAN in bold letters, and the date.

Choosing your company name is an important decision. I chose "Gaskell Associates Consulting Engineers." Most consulting engineering firms in my area were similarly named, using the last name of the PE. When I later became an "S" Corporation, I changed it to "Gaskell Associates, LTD–Consulting Engineers." Later, when my firm was bought by Thielsch Engineering, we became "Gaskell Associates Consulting Engineers – A Division of Thielsch Engineering."

I have a close friend, David Doyle, PE, who named his mechanical engineering firm "Creative Environment Corporation." It had the initial disadvantage of not identifying him. But it had the benefit of being somewhat descriptive of the type of work that they did and a name more easily assumed by a future purchaser. In fact, Thielsch Engineering also bought this firm, combined it with mine, and the division is now called "Creative Environment – A Division of Thielsch Engineering."

It is important to be sure that your proposed company name is unique, at least in the areas that you plan to practice, now and in the future. You or your attorney should check and avoid pitfalls such as another business already having claimed your name, trademark, and website address/URL.

Once you are a registered professional engineer, "PE" can be used as a suffix to your official name; for example, John Q. Jones, PE. If you do business under any other name, you may need to register that name with the appropriate authorities. This is called "doing business as" (DBA) name or "fictitious business name." Surprisingly, this requirement would also apply to a name like "John Q. Jones, PE, Consulting Engineers." Review with your attorney.

Table of Contents

Do this last. Use the above list starting with Executive Summary and including page numbers. Provide a sub-list of the Supplemental Material. Add appropriate sections, if fitting for your firm.

Executive Summary

Do this after the other sections are complete. It is the most <u>important</u> section and the only one that many people may read. But if you do a good job on the other sections, this one will write itself.

Business Description

Describe what services your firm will provide, the kinds of projects, and the types of clients. Expand upon "why" these services are needed during each of the "phases" of a project. Assume that the reader knows little or nothing about consulting engineering.

My Qualifications (or "The Management Team")

List your name, title, and proposed job description (brief) here. Also, include the same for your partners and any employees. At the end of each, state "See attached resume," and enclose them as the following pages in this section or in Supplemental Materials.

Ownership Agreement

If you will have partners, include this section. Describe your planned legal structure (Partnership, "S" Corporation, etc.). Also, meet with an impartial attorney (who will probably be your company attorney), and prepare a Partnership or Shareholders Agreement, which should include the following: names of partners/shareholders and percent of ownership, financial commitment of each (initially and at a later date), authority of each, role of each in business operations, technical and business contribution of each to firm's consulting services, authority of each, signing of checks, division of profits and losses, draws or salaries, absence/disability, death of a partner, non-compete upon departure, settlement of disputes, employee management, etc.

Operations Plan

Describe your proposed operation in paragraph form. Include hours of operation, who will receive guests, how phones will be answered, and a detailed job description of you, your partners, and staff.

Cover how projects will be handled: meetings with clients, production of the drawings, technical specifications, bidding requirements, addenda, award of contract, shop drawing review, clarifications, job site meetings, progress reviews, approval of requisitions, punch lists, and project close out.

Legal, Records/Taxes & Insurance

See Chapter 8. Include the names of the professionals that you have contacted and plan to use.

Marketing Plans

Summarize Chapters 9 and 10 and analyze your competition.

Start-Up Costs

Describe how you arrived at your "Start-Up Cost Estimate," and include your completed Figure **4-1** here or in Supplemental Materials.

Cash Outflow Projections

Describe how you arrived at your "First Year Cash Outflow" estimate, and include your completed Figure **4-3** here or in Supplemental Materials.

Cash Inflow Projections

Describe how you arrived at your "First Year Cash Inflow" projection, and include your completed Figure **4-5** here or in Supplemental Materials.

Cash Flow Analysis

Describe how you arrived at your "Cash Flow Analysis," and include your completed Figure **5-1** here or in Supplemental Materials.

Balance Sheets

Describe how you prepared your "Balance Sheets," and include your completed Figure **5-3** here or in Supplemental Materials.

Financing Overview & Funding Needs

List your "start-up-funding" here, including the source of each contribution. Include savings being invested, gifts promised, if any, and loans promised (or anticipated). Reconcile this with your "First Year Cash Flow Analysis" – Figure **5-1**. Explain discrepancies, if any.

Supplemental Materials

Include the attachments to which you have referred at the end of this "Business Plan." Also consider including other supporting information, such as Letters of Reference, Letters of Commitment from financing sources, copies of bank statements, etc.

DECIDE

Review your completed "Business Plan" and make your "go/no go/or wait" decision. This review should include your partners and all spouses/significant others, if any.

THE FINAL TOUCH

Carefully proofread your Business Plan. Have at least three people who you trust review and "critically" comment.

Have a number of copies professionally printed and bound.

This will be your "Key Tool" in seeking financing and a line of credit, both for start-up and for cash flow needs.

ADDITIONAL INFORMATION

Go to your local library or book store and look for books on writing a Business Plan. Most include examples of Business Plans.

Go to www.sba.gov, the Small Business Administration Web Site. The log in process is not easy, and you need to dig through many layers to find what you are looking for, but there is a lot of good information on business plans.

From the Start Page, place your cursor on "Start & Manage" (near the top left). Then, select the second item, "Create your Business Plan." You will find 10 short articles about each section of their proposed Business Plan. In the upper right, there is a step-by-step tool for you to write your plan and save it on this secure site. (No one will ever guess your password.)

This website also has great information on all aspects of starting a business.

OUTLINE SUMMARY

- **What is a business plan?** A "Business Plan" is a formal statement of business goals, reasons they are attainable, and plans for reaching them. It should also contain background information about the organization attempting to reach those goals.

- **Why is a business plan important?**
  - It is the "structure" of your practice which precisely defines your company and identifies your goals.
  - It will organize your thoughts and will give you a "game plan."
  - It will help you make a "go/no go/or wait" decision.
  - It will help you in forecasting funding needs and securing "financing."

- **Be careful and realistic:** A "Business Plan" is one of the most important and frequently overlooked steps in the process of starting an engineering practice.

- **Make it your game plan:** Your Business Plan defines your company and its goals, helps you (and your spouse/partners) make a "go/no go/or wait" decision, and aids in forecasting financial needs and securing financing.

- **Update:** Look at your Business Plan both monthly and annually. Compare projections to actual and adjust expectations accordingly or modify actions to compensate.

- **Company name:** Carefully choose your company name considering both how it identifies you and the future salability of your practice.

- **Key tool:** Your Business Plan will be critically important in seeking financial support, financing, and a line of credit for start-up and cash flow needs.

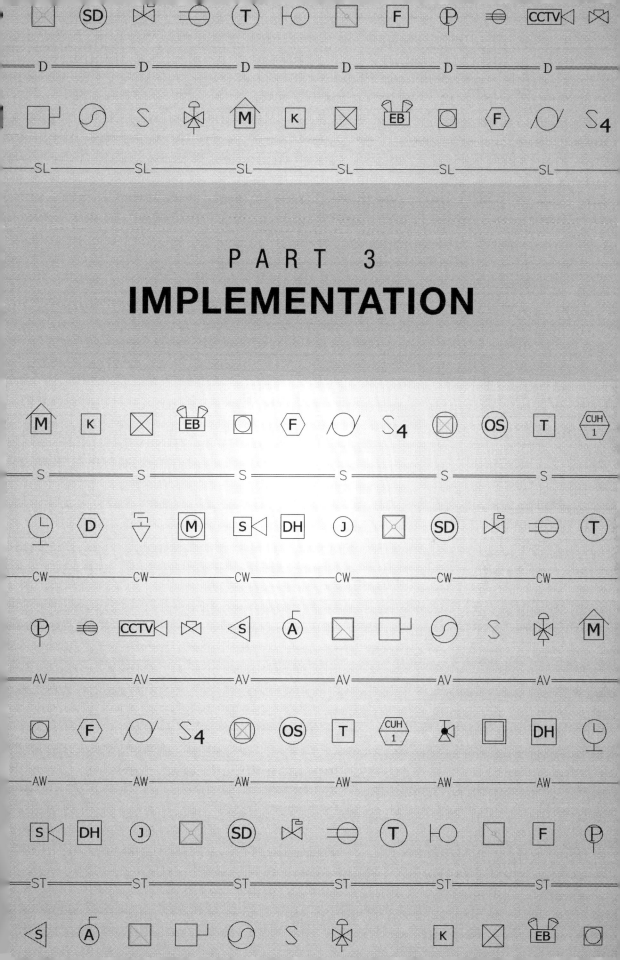

PART 3
IMPLEMENTATION

CHAPTER 7

CASTING OFF
(STARTING YOUR
OWN PRACTICE)

INTRODUCTION

You will discover why checklists are your friends: they remind you of all the necessary steps and help you avoid the missed steps. The "Pre-Start-Up Checklist" will reveal the many necessary and time consuming details that can be done in advance. The "Final Start-Up Checklist" will uncover which things should only be done after you have Cast Off. Learn the secret that Benjamin Franklin and the Boy Scouts shared.

GENERAL

"Casting Off" is like starting on a long sea journey; make sure that your vessel is sea worthy. Be prepared for the voyage by reviewing the "Pre-Start-Up Checklist" and the "Final Start-Up Checklist." Discover how to avoid "strageties" (this is not a misspelling, it is a new word—read on).

I assure you that if you have followed my advice, this will be the trip of your life and lead to an exceptional engineering practice, career satisfaction, and financial security. *Bon voyage* and calm seas.

"PRE-START-UP CHECKLIST"

- *Verify "Ownership Agreement."
- *Verify "Cash Availability."
- *Apply for a "Loan" and/or a "Line of Credit" (if needed).
- Prepare a realistic "Time Table" for all activities.
- Update insurance quotes.
- Prepare your "Company Brochure."
- Prepare your "Business Announcement."
- Select your "Letterhead & Business Cards."
- Plan your "Website."
- Update your "Client List."
- Make a list of "Library Materials" needed (catalogs, etc.).
- Prepare your "Standard Documents."
- Prepare your "Operations Manual."
- Prepare "CAD & BIM Files" and standards.
- Finalize "Rental Space" selection.

It is important that you realize that the tasks in the "Pre-Start-Up Checklist" will likely take 2 to 6 months in your spare time, if done carefully and thoroughly.

(*Do not proceed to the "FINAL START-UP CHECKLIST" until the first three items in the "PRE-START-UP CHECKLIST" are completed and approved.)

*Verify "Ownership Agreement"

If you have partners, your attorney helped you prepare an Ownership Agreement as part of your Business Plan. Now that you are "Casting Off," each of you (and your significant others) should rereview this and each of you should sign it to be sure that everyone is committed.

*Verify "Cash Availability"

If part of your start-up cash is a gift or a personal loan, verify that it is readily available. Also, if you have a spouse, make sure that there has not been a change of heart. If you have partners, be sure that they do the same. At this point, it would be best if everyone provided "Proof of Cash."

*Apply for a "Loan" and/or "Line of Credit" (if needed)

See Chapter 5 – Financial Analysis.

Prepare a realistic "Time Table" for all activities

If you are going to work out of your house, you can probably get everything done in a month. Otherwise, it could take three months or longer. Don't spend money before you have to. *When I first started my practice, I bought a "Hanging Plan Rack." It was nice, and it was on sale for only $400. I felt that I needed it for easy access to plans of projects "under construction." I didn't stop to think that it would be quite a while before my projects were "under construction," and I already had two large "plan files" (used to store "original drawings") that were mostly empty and would have easily served the purpose. This was a significant portion of my "Start-Up Cash" to waste on an unnecessary purchase.*

Don't give notice at your present place of employment too early, and be prepared that the boss might immediately "show you the door." You don't want to be unemployed for three months before starting your own business. And you don't want to start practicing before you have professional liability insurance. Make sure that you have copies of all your files before giving notice. Also, don't blab to the other employees about your plans. "Friends" can be jealous, and the boss will find out.

If you have partners, make a "pact" to not consider counter offers from your present employers or from anyone else.

Update insurance quotes

See Chapter 8 – Legal, Accounting & Insurance.

Prepare your "Company Brochure"

See Chapter 9 – Marketing Materials.

Prepare your "Business Announcement"

See Chapter 9 – Marketing Materials.

Select a "Letterhead & Business Cards"

See Chapter 9 – Marketing Materials.

Plan your "Website"

Prepare website content.

Update your "Client List"

See Chapter 4 – Financial Forecasting, Chapter 6 – Business Plan, and Chapter 9 – Marketing Materials.

Make a list of "Library Materials" needed (catalogs, etc.)

At my office, I had a separate "library" with many bookshelves containing large manufacture's catalogs. I realize that much of this information is available "online," but you need to make a list of any that you need in your office library. Don't forget to record the information regarding the Manufacturer's Representative. But don't make the mistake of seeking your own catalogs too soon; salesmen are the biggest blabbers around. Also, obtain "hard copies" of code books to which you need immediate access.

Prepare your "Standard Documents"

Obtain copies of contracts used by your present employer and as many as you can from others. Use these as "guides" in preparing your own. Don't plagiarize the work of others. The "Terms and Conditions" (usually printed on the back) are of particular importance. See Chapter 10 – Marketing Methods & Chapter 13 – Operations Manual.

Prepare your "Operations Manual"

Your Operations Manual is the "guidebook" to your engineering practice and will be a major ingredient in your firm's success. Prepare it now. See Chapter 13 – Operations Manual.

Prepare "CAD & BIM Files" and standards

Make sure that you have copies of all standard and special details, legends, notes, etc. that you will need. And remember that you may not have access to the company computer once your employer finds out that you are leaving. Again, don't plagiarize the work of others. Also, just because you may have created the document doesn't mean that you own it. If you created it in the course of your employment, it is likely the property of your employer.

Finalize "Rental Space" selection

Compare spaces currently available. Negotiate rent, fit-out costs, and lease terms. But don't sign a lease yet.

"FINAL START-UP CHECKLIST"
(Do only after the first three items in the "PRE-START-UP CHECKLIST" are completed and approved.)

- "Rent/Lease" office space
- Deal with "legal matters"
- Obtain "General Insurance"
- Obtain "Professional Liability Insurance"
- Meet with your "CPA"
- Order check writing system or accounting software
- Complete Office "Fit-Out"
- Purchase & Installation of Office "Phone System"
- Buy/Rent "Office Furniture"
- Buy/Rent "Office Equipment"
- Buy computer software (including CAD & BIM)
- Buy "Office Supplies"
- Print "Company Brochure"
- Print "Business Announcement"
- Print "Letterhead & Business Cards"
- Hire a website designer
- "Move in & Setup"

"Rent/Lease" office space
Have your attorney review the lease before you sign. But remember that attorneys are known as "The Deal Killers." So, make sure that their requests are reasonable and important. In any case, don't rush into it.

Deal with "legal matters"
Meet with your attorney and do the legal work required. See Chapter 8 – Legal, Accounting & Insurance.

Obtain "General Insurance"
Contact your insurance agent. See Chapter 8 – Legal, Accounting & Insurance.

Obtain "Professional Liability Insurance"
See Chapter 8 – Legal, Accounting & Insurance.

Meet with your "CPA"

See Chapter 8 – Legal, Accounting & Insurance.

Order check writing system or accounting software

Follow the recommendations of your CPA. See Chapter 8 – Legal, Accounting & Insurance.

Complete Office "Fit-Out"

Your goal should be to buy your own office space in about five years. So, don't go overboard on this rental space. Most meetings will be held elsewhere (at client's office, job sites, etc.). You don't need the best carpeting, but you don't want it to look shabby after six months. (Proper carpet maintenance is a good investment.) Are there "hardwood floors" under the existing carpeting? Can some spaces be left open without walls or partitions? (This will also minimize HVAC changes.) Think economically and conserve cash.

Purchase & Installation of Office "Phone System"

See Chapter 4 – Financial Forecasting.

Buy/Rent "Office Furniture"

See Chapter 4 – Financial Forecasting.

Buy/Rent "Office Equipment"

See Chapter 4 – Financial Forecasting.

Buy computer software (including CAD & BIM)

See Chapter 4 – Financial Forecasting.

Buy "Office Supplies"

See Chapter 4 – Financial Forecasting.

Print "Company Brochure"

See Chapter 9 – Marketing Materials.

Print "Business Announcement"

See Chapter 9 – Marketing Materials.

Print "Letterhead & Business Cards"
See Chapter 9 – Marketing Materials.

Hire a website designer
In the internet age, a professional-looking website and search engine optimization is a must. Don't try to do it on your own. See Chapter 10 – Marketing Methods.

"Move-in & Setup"

FINAL THOUGHTS
The survival rate of new businesses is low; only about half survive five years. The Boy Scout motto is "Be Prepared," good advice in life and when starting a new venture. My favorite historical figure, Benjamin Franklin, is credited with saying, "By failing to prepare, you are preparing to fail." The secret to success is researching and writing a careful Business Plan and updating it annually to correct failed strategies (my friend Brian/BA calls these "strageties"), institute new ideas, and implement new technology. At your first year anniversary, let me know how it is going.

OUTLINE SUMMARY

- **"PRE-START-UP CHECKLIST"**
  - *Verify "Ownership Agreement"
  - *Verify "Cash Availability"
  - *Apply for "Loan" and/or "Line of Credit" (if needed)
  - Prepare a realistic "Time Table" for all activities
  - Update insurance quotes
  - Prepare your "Company Brochure"
  - Prepare your "Business Announcement"
  - Select your "Letterhead & Business Cards"
  - Plan your "Website"
  - Update your "Client List"
  - Make a list of "Library Materials" needed (catalogs, etc.)
  - Prepare your "Standard Documents"
  - Prepare your "Operations Manual"
  - Prepare "CAD & BIM Files" and standards
  - Finalize "Rental Space" Selection

- **"FINAL START-UP CHECKLIST".**
  (*Do only after the first three items in the "PRE-START-UP CHECKLIST" are completed and approved.)
  - "Rent/Lease" office space
  - Deal with "legal matters"
  - Obtain "General Insurance"
  - Obtain "Professional Liability Insurance"
  - Meet with your "CPA"
  - Order check writing system or accounting software
  - Complete Office "Fit-Out"
  - Purchase & Installation of Office "Phone System"
  - Buy/Rent "Office Furniture"
  - Buy/Rent "Office Equipment"
  - Buy computer software (including CAD & BIM)
  - Buy "Office Supplies"
  - Print "Company Brochure"
  - Print "Business Announcement"
  - Print your "Letterhead & Business Cards"
  - Hire a website designer
  - "Move in & Setup"

PART 4
MANAGING YOUR FIRM

CHAPTER 8

LEGAL, ACCOUNTING & INSURANCE

INTRODUCTION

You will learn that the "business entity" that you choose for your engineering practice will have major legal and tax implications. Discover which government agency will help you to choose the best structure for your situation. Find out the special liability issues that PEs have of which some attorneys are unaware. Detect concerns that are often overlooked when choosing a business structure. Uncover how to save money using common sense.

You will realize that all accountants are not CPAs and why your firm should hire a CPA. Discern the "tax" implications of your "business structure" and which method of accounting, "cash" or "accrual," usually works better for a small professional practice. Learn how careful "time tracking" will benefit your practice by uncovering inaccuracies and inefficiencies. Understand when to progress from "manual" time tracking to "off-the-shelf" solutions and then to "customized" accounting software.

Hear about what type of "general" insurance all consulting engineering firms need and which may be optional. Understand why you need "professional liability/errors and omissions" insurance, what is meant by a "claims-made" basis, and when you need "retroactive" coverage. Find out which employee benefit you can't overlook and the percent the employee might be expected to contribute.

LEGAL

Business Structure

Learn about business structures at the Small Business Administration's Website (www.sba.gov). They have articles describing each of the following types:

Sole Proprietorship

A sole proprietorship is the most basic type of business to establish. You alone own the company and are responsible for its assets and liabilities.

Limited Liability Company

Designed to provide the limited liability features of a corporation and the tax efficiencies and operational flexibility of a partnership or sole proprietorship.

Corporation

A corporation is more complex and is generally suggested for larger, established companies with multiple employees.

Partnership

A partnership is an arrangement in which parties agree to cooperate to advance their mutual interests. There are several different types of partnerships which depend on the nature of the arrangement and partner responsibility for the business.

"S" Corporation

An "S" corporation is similar to a "C" corporation but taxation is done only at the personal level.

Initial Meeting

Look for a small law firm that regularly handles "start-up work" for small business. Try to get recommendations from friends (not competitors) at other small engineering firms. Call the law firm, ask to speak with one of the "principal" attorneys, describe the engineering practice that you are starting, ask to setup an initial meeting, and enquire regarding the fee (if any) for the initial meeting.

At the meeting, ask which business ownership "structures" you should initially consider. Some Professional Registration Laws require all owners/partners be licensed members of the profession. If this would be a problem for your firm, make sure that your attorney checks the appropriate laws. Be certain that the attorney is aware that each PE who stamps/seals documents cannot avoid personal liability for his errors and omissions by having a corporate business structure. However, being a corporation may shield individuals from certain types of contract liability.

Also, ask for an estimated cost for the initial paperwork (both legal filing and attorney fees). Initial legal work is a "start-up" cost. Later, there will be occasional phone questions for which you may or may not be charged. However, there will be legal costs as complicated questions or issues arise. The attorney may also be able to recommend CPAs for you to consider.

Legally Starting Your Business

When you are ready to "Cast Off," one of the first steps is to take care of legal matters. Is the attorney that you met with during the planning stages the right one for you? Did you like him? Did he seem competent? Were his fees reasonable? If unsure, interview other law firms. If ready to proceed, set up a meeting including all of your partners. At the start of the meeting, verify what you were told at the "Initial Meeting" (form of business ownership, associated legal and filing fees, and other expected costs).

Review the advantages/disadvantages of each possible form of business ownership again to be sure that you are making the right initial decision. Ask about ongoing legal work that would be expected in your case.

Don't forget to consider:

- Your CPA's input.
- Has another business already claimed your proposed company name or one very similar? Try Googling it.
- Is the web address/URL available? Try Google, again. Try godaddy.com.
- Is a "fictitious name" registration required?

One final thought concerning your attorney: Every week, questions and situations come up when practicing engineering that could be classified as a "legal matter." If you constantly call your attorney, he will be sailing on a luxury yacht while you go bankrupt. Don't overlook the true need to get legal advice, but most times you can use "common sense." In Figure **12-4**, I list the Terms and Conditions that I printed on the back of my standard fee proposals. When you read them, you will think: "No one would ever agree to these." But, surprisingly, very few clients ever objected to any of these Terms and Conditions. Read them again, and ask yourself the question: "If any of these requirements were dismissed by a court, would I have been better off without them?" I think that they avoided problems and frivolous law suits, and I eluded painful legal bills by using my own judgment. If in doubt, consult with your attorney.

ACCOUNTING

Initial Meeting

An accountant is the other essential advisor on your management team. The same recommendations as outlined for the meeting with your attorney apply here.

Not all accountants are Certified Public Accountants (CPAs). Anyone, regardless of education, experience, or competence can call themselves an "accountant." CPAs are tested and licensed, are more professional, and will garner more respect when dealing with government agencies. When I started my practice, my CPA set me up with a "one-write" check book and spread sheets with columns for each of the expenses. I photocopied the spreadsheets for him at the end of each month, and he compiled them at the end of the year and did my taxes. In the "computer age," programs like "QuickBooks" or "Sage" may be more appropriate. In any case, there will be initial, monthly, and yearly charges from your accountant. Ask for an estimate.

When you meet with your CPA, review the attorney's initial recommendations. Some forms of ownership require a great deal of costly work for your accountant, which needs to be taken into consideration.

Your accountant may be able to refer you to a bank officer who may get your loan application approved based on the accountant's recommendation.

Taxes

Your form of business ownership will greatly impact your taxes. The "cash" method of accounting, rather than the "accrual" method, usually works better regarding taxes for a small professional practice. Certain corporate forms of ownership require that the "accrual" method be used. Regardless, your accountant can easily provide reports both ways to give you an accurate picture of profits and losses.

It is important that you remit payroll taxes and workers' compensation payments at the required intervals. Your accountant or your payroll service will assist you with this.

You must also send in both federal and state income tax estimates on time. If you are a "C" Corporation, your company accountant should estimate your taxes and provide the necessary filing forms, and your company writes the checks. If you are a sole proprietor, partnership, or an "S" corporation, this is your personal responsibility. It often makes sense to use the same accountant for both business and personal needs. In either case, your accountant will appreciate receiving your yearly personal income tax information timely, more than a month before the filling deadline.

Project Tracking

One of the utmost important aspects of your business is carefully keeping track of your time. On "hourly" projects, you need this information for billing; on "fixed-fee" projects, you don't. However, if you don't keep track of time or if you don't eventually add it up, you won't know the winners from the losers. Why is this important?

> The type of project may require more time; knowing this would allow you to increase your fee on the next similar project or to pass up the project.

> Your project manager may be inefficient; knowing this allows you to give him more training, assign him to less complicated projects, or to replace him with someone else.

> The client may be too difficult or demanding; knowing this allows you to negotiate both scope and fee on the next project. It is surprising how less demanding a client can become when faced with the added costs. This problem can also be handled with "Assumptions & Exceptions" in your contract, i.e., "We assume four meetings with you during design; add $xxx for each additional." Also, remember that you just can't make money working for some clients; if you can't correct the problem, let your competitor deal with it.

> The project owner/manager may be too difficult or demanding; the solution is the same as described above.

> The scope may "creep"; knowing this, it may not be too late to bill. (But don't do so without discussing extra charges with the client beforehand.) In any case, it may be time to have a talk with your project manager so this problem can be avoided in the future.

My first year in private practice, almost all of my projects were "fixed-fee," and I viewed filling out a time card as unpaid work. I needed every job to meet expenses. So, if I worked for "slave wages," it was better than no wages, and I didn't pay myself overtime. But if I had known which clients/projects were the winners and which were the losers, I could have tried to promote more winners.

Keeping track of "non-project" time is also important. Examples include general office, sick time, holidays, and fee proposals. See Time Cards and Time Card Instructions, **A-2** and **A-2 (I)**, in Chapter 13 – Operations Manual. *If I had realized how much time I was spending on general office, I might have hired a second person sooner.*

Manual Tracking

Have your secretary/clerical start a TIME SHEET for each "project" and each "non-project" category of time. List week ending dates on the left, a column for each employee across the top, and transfer the "Time Card" information weekly. Close out the month at the end of the week closest to the completion of the calendar month, and add up the hours for the month and the hours to date. Try to bill so that your client will have the bill by the 1st of the next month to avoid waiting an extra month for payment.

Also, at the close of the month, each project manager should estimate the "percent complete" of the project "phase" for each project that time was charged to during that month. The "Partner in Charge" of that project should verify the percent complete. On "fixed-fee" projects, monthly billing should be based on this percent. Of course, in "multi-discipline" firms, each trade is estimated and billed on its own percent complete. Spread sheets (like Excel) now make this process simpler and more accurate.

It is also important for you to compare the billing to the budget of hours monthly. If a project has expended more hours than you can be billed, it is losing money. Try to find out why. Was there an increase in scope? Maybe it is not too late to bill. Make sure that your project manager knows to bring scope changes to your attention <u>before</u> doing the work. Whatever the reason, knowing about it allows you to account for it on the next similar project.

Off-the-Shelf Accounting Software

The above described "manual" system works well for very small firms. But once you are billing for three or more people, it is time to consider getting accounting software. The most common "starter systems" are inexpensive. Review options with your accountant before buying the software.

QuickBooks and Sage 50 (formerly Peach Tree) are two of the most popular accounting software systems. They are off-the-shelf packages for only a few hundred dollars. Both are "single" entry systems; the programs do the double entry. Both can do "accrual method" and "cash method" reporting and have integrated accounts receivable, accounts payable, and general ledger functions. These are not as flexible as the more expensive systems, and your bookkeeper can make changes to data that is not "tracked" and can cause heartburn for your accountant. If you trust your bookkeeper, you will find these systems to be a leap past manual billing.

Customizable Accounting Software

The previously described systems will serve the needs of most small firms, but if your firm has special needs, you may want to consider a more customizable system. Examples of special needs are unique situations such as progress billing, calculations, special billing rate situations (i.e., for government work), or prevailing wage tracking.

As your firm grows, you may want to consider an industry software package with "all the bells and whistles"; more reports with more details. But you may need a software consultant to set it up, customize the system, and provide ongoing support. Also, you may need a full-time bookkeeper to enter the data and print reports. If someone actually reads these reports, interoperates them correctly, and implements policies to make improvements, these systems can be worthwhile, especially for larger firms. Unless you have special needs, wait until you outgrow the inexpensive options. I found the "Ageing of Receivables" and the "Budgeted vs. Actual hours" reports to be the most useful.

At the point that you are considering customizable accounting software, you might want to contact a company called "Find Accounting Software": www.findaccountingsoftware.com, (800) 827-1151. They are independent software systems advisors with information on 3,000 software products in 86 categories. They do not receive a commission; they are paid an annual fee from the companies listed. You can simply call them, have a 10–15 minute conversation regarding your needs and budget, and within 24 hours you will receive information from them or their vendors regarding the programs that most closely match your requirements.

Alternatively, you can go to their website. From the home page, select INDUSTRY, and then select Engineering. The Engineering page has a lot of great general information followed by a list of about 50 programs for engineering firms. You can click on each of these for a detailed description of the product. Instead, I recommend that you review the general information, and then call the above number.

INSURANCE

Your Insurance Broker

An insurance broker differs from an insurance agent in that a broker is considered an agent of the insured even though they receive a commission from the insurance company.

A broker may sell the products of a number of insurers, whereas an insurance agent has the insurer as his principal and works in the interest of the insurer (insurance company) and not the insured (you).

I recommend working with a well-established, "independent" insurance broker. They can get answers to your questions and personally assist you in the event of a claim. Your insurance broker can usually handle both your "general" and "professional liability" needs. It is always prudent for your insurance broker to get quotes from two or three different insurance companies.

The more coverage you purchase, the higher the cost. So, you need to be the "risk manager" for your company and only buy the type and amount of coverage that you think is prudent, within budget constraints.

As a consulting engineering firm, you will need three basic types of insurance: "general liability" (1 or more policies), "professional liability" (a single policy), and people (health) insurance.

General Liability

The needs of each professional practice is different. But these are some of the most common types of general liability coverage:

- "Comprehensive Liability" – covers losses at your place of business related to bodily injury or damage to the property of others, including medical and defense.
- "Automobile Liability" – covers losses while you or your employees use a car for business purposes. (Make sure that each employee has their own automobile policy; require copies annually for your file.)
- "Fire & Theft Liability" – covers your office and its contents.
- "Business Interruption" – covers the loss of revenue in the event that your premises or files are destroyed.
- "Personal Disability" – pays a monthly amount if a covered person is temporarily, permanently, fully, or partially disabled.

- "Partnership Insurance" – allows for a deceased partner's interest to be purchased by the surviving partners.
- "Employee Theft" – protects you from the bookkeeper "cooking the books," for example.

I feel that for general insurance, as a minimum, you need comprehensive, auto, fire, and theft. After the first year, consider expanding coverage.

Professional Liability Insurance

Engineers always try to do their best work, but mistakes sometimes occur, resulting in lawsuits.

Professional liability insurance, more commonly known as errors and omissions (E&O), is a form of liability insurance that helps protect professional advice and service (providing individuals and companies) from bearing the full cost of defending against a negligence claim made and damages awarded in such a civil lawsuit.

The coverage focuses on alleged failure to perform on the part of, financial loss caused by, and error or omission in the services provided. These are potential causes for legal action that would not be covered by a more general liability insurance policy which addresses more direct forms of harm. Professional liability coverage also provides for the defense costs when legal action turns out to be groundless. Coverage does not include criminal prosecution nor a wide range of potential liabilities under civil law, which may be subject to other forms of insurance.

Professional liability insurance is often required under contract by your clients. Professional liability insurance policies are generally setup based on a "claims-made" basis, meaning that the policy only covers claims made during the policy period. Claims which may relate to incidents occurring before the coverage was active will not be covered, although some policies may have a retroactive date.

Coverage should be continued for as long as the policyholder provides covered services, plus the span of any applicable statute of limitations. Cancelling the policy before this time would, in effect, make it as if the insured never had coverage since any client could bring any case with regard to any such services that occurred before the statute of limitations cut-off point. A break in coverage could result in what is called a "gap in coverage," which is the loss of all prior acts.

When you retire or close your business, you should purchase tail or nose insurance. "Tail" or "extended reporting" endorsements cover events that occur while the policy is in force but are reported to the carrier after the policy terminates. Purchasing tail coverage from the present carrier effectively converts the claims-made policy into an occurrence policy. "Prior acts" or "nose" coverage transfers the retroactive date for an old policy to a new insurance carrier—eliminating the need to purchase tail coverage from the last carrier. Nose coverage is sometimes less expensive than purchasing tail coverage from the old carrier. Tail coverage costs 2–3 times the expiring premium. A company that purchases your firm usually pays the cost of either "tail" or "nose" coverage as part of the "Purchase and Sales" agreement.

I have included a list of companies that offer professional liability coverage. See Figure **8-1** "Professional Liability Insurers." I encourage you to consider both coverage and services provided, in addition to price.

PROFESSIONAL LIABILITY INSURERS

ACE USA Insurance
601 So. Figueroa St., 15th Fl.
Los Angeles, CA 90017
(213) 833-3100

AEIC
2056 Westings Ave., Suite 20
Naperville, IL 60563
(800) 437-2342

Argo Pro Insurance
2000 S. Batavia St.
Geneva, IL 60134
(800) 447-4626

Arrowhead Design Insurance
99 Pacific St., Suite 155F
Monterey, CA 93940
(831) 333-9840

Aspen Insurance
590 Madison Ave., 7th Fl.
New York, NY 10022
(646) 502-1012

AXIS Insurance
300 Connell Dr., Suite 8000
Berkeley Heights, NJ 07922
(908) 673-2963

Beazley Insurance
141 Tremont St., Suite 1200
Boston, MA 02111
(617) 239-2600

Catlin Design Professional
1331 N. California Blvd.
Walnut Creek, CA 94596
(925) 927-2239

CNA/ Schinnerer & Co.
2 Wisconsin Circle
Chevy Chase, MD 20815
(301) 961-9800

Euclid Managers Insurance
234 Spring Lake Dr.
Itasca, IL 60143
(630) 238-1900

Hanover Insurance Group
333 W. Pierce Rd., Suite 300
Itasca, IL 60143
(630) 760-3045

HCC Specialty Insurance
2300 Clayton Rd., Suite 1100
Concord CA 94520
(925) 685-1600

James River Insurance
PO Box 27648
Richmond, VA 23261
(804) 289-2700

Lexington Insurance Co.
100 Summer St.
Boston, MA 02110
(617) 330-8564

Liberty Int. Underwriters
LIU USA, 18th Fl.
55 Water St.
New York, NY 10041
(212) 208-4100

Markel Insurance
10 Parkway North
Deerfield, IL 60015
(847) 572-6000

Navigators Management Co.
6011 University Blvd., St. 280
Ellicott City, MD 21043
(443) 364-5938

RLI Insurance Co.
150 Monument Rd., St. 605
Bala Cynwyd, PA 19004
(610) 664-8700

Travelers Insurance
111 Schilling Rd.
Hunt Valley, MD 21031
(443) 353-2263

XL Insurance
30 Ragsdale Dr., Suite 201
Monterey CA 93940
(800) 227-8533

FIGURE 8-1

From the start of my practice, I insured with the CNA/Schinnerer Professional Liability Insurance Program, and I stayed with them for my tail coverage when I sold my practice. They have been partnered with both NSPE and AIA for over 40 years. Go to www.shinnerer.com, www.nspe.org, and www.aia.org to check them out.

I stayed with CNA/Schinnerer primarily for their "pre-claims assistance" and their "guidelines." In my over 35 years of practice, I had a few situations that I thought might result in a lawsuit. I contacted the insurer (through my insurance broker), and they connected me with a great local lawyer who specialized in construction claims. I met with the lawyer two or three times and, fortunately, the suits never materialized. There was no charge to me, and my insurance premiums did not increase.

Four times a year, CNA/Schinnerer produces "guidelines," a four page document with short articles on improving your practice. I ended up with a thick binder of these and almost always found something, in every issue, to share with my staff.

People Coverage

This category includes, among others:

- Group Health
- Dental
- Profit Sharing

- Individual Disability
- 401k
- Group Life

Group Health is the one area that you can't initially overlook. The others can wait until you are on your feet.

Shop for a plan that accepts most doctors and hospitals and covers when traveling out of state. To hold down costs, seek a plan with high deductibles.

Employees should pay part of the costs through payroll deductions. For a "start-up" company, consider having employees contribute 30% for themselves and 40% for their families. But try to be more generous as the company proves it self. Also, these percentages may have to be adjusted for your company to be competitive in your job market. Consider compensating an employee who, instead, uses a spouse's program. I used to reimburse about 50% of what I was saving.

OUTLINE SUMMARY

- **Business structure:** The "business structure" that you choose for your engineering practice will have major legal and tax implications.

- **SBA:** The Small Business Administration's website (www.sba.gov) has helpful articles describing the major types of business entities.

- **Legal:** Seek a recommendation to a small law firm and ask for an initial meeting; don't be afraid to enquire about the cost.

- **Personal liability:** Make sure that your attorney is aware that each PE who stamps/seals documents cannot avoid personal liability for his errors and omissions by having a corporate business structure.

- **Considerations:** Don't forget to consider your CPA's input, same or similar company names in use, availability of web address/URL, or "fictitious name" filing.

- **Evaluate legal needs:** Don't hesitate to consult your attorney for important legal matters, but avoid costly consultations on trivial things.

- **CPA:** Look for a small CPA firm (not just an accountant) that regularly handles "start-up work" for small businesses.

- **Accounting method:** The "cash" method of accounting, rather than the "accrual" method, usually works better regarding taxes for a small professional practice.

- **Track time:** An important aspect of your business is carefully keeping track of time; it is the only thing that you have to sell. Tracking time will help you to make more accurate budgets, discover inefficiencies, identify difficult clients, and uncover "scope creep."

- **Simple time tracking:** Transfer time card hours to project summary sheets and summarize monthly. Manual tracking of time will be easier and more accurate using computer spread sheets.

- **Off-the-shelf software:** As your firm expands, consider getting "off-the-shelf" accounting software; QuickBooks and Sage 50 are popular choices.

- **Customizable software:** If you have special billing needs or when you grow larger, it may be worth investigating "customizable" accounting software. The Accounts Receivable Aging report and Budgeted vs. Actual hours are most useful.

- **Insurance:** You need to be the "risk manager" for your company when purchasing insurance.

- **Insurance needs:** General insurance needs for each professional practice can be different but usually include comprehensive, auto, and fire and theft.

- **Errors & omissions:** Engineers always try to do their best work, but mistakes sometimes occur, resulting in lawsuits. Professional liability insurance (PLI), more commonly known as errors and omissions (E&O), is a form of liability insurance that helps protect professionals.

- **Claims made:** PLI policies are generally setup on a "claims-made" basis, meaning that the policy only covers claims made during the policy period. If you change insurance companies, make sure that you are covered retroactively. I encourage you to consider both coverage and services provided, in addition to price.

- **Group health insurance:** Health insurance is the one area that you can't initially overlook. For a "start-up" company, consider having employees contribute 30% for themselves and 40% for their families.

CHAPTER 9

MARKETING MATERIALS

INTRODUCTION

Find out how to prepare your business announcement, letterhead, business cards, and brochure distinct from those of your competitors. Learn how to make your mailing list one of your most important promotional tools and why to include more than just existing and potential clients. Discover the lists and forms that your new practice will need, and discern a simple way to avoid construction headaches. Most importantly, understand the secret to gaining a reputation as an "expert" in your field.

GENERAL

I think that the two chapters on MARKETING are the <u>most</u> important chapters in this book. Finding and keeping clients is the key to success. Most people, especially engineers, are "shy." Get over it!

While attending college, I worked two summers selling encyclopedias door-to-door. In the process, I gained confidence.

I am not suggesting a second job, but you do need to get over your timidity. Your activities described under "Get Know & Gain Credentials" in Chapter 2 should have provided many opportunities to meet new people and occasions for public speaking. If you followed my advice, you are ready for marketing.

The following is a list of documents to prepare once you have made the decision to open your own practice. But don't actually get them printed until you are ready to "Cast Off" (See Chapter 7).

BASIC MARKETING MATERIALS

Business Announcement

Your business announcement should look and feel like a wedding invitation, with fine paper (perhaps matching your letterhead) and raised letters. It should include the words "consulting engineers," state the names of partners, and list specialties offered.

Letterhead

When I started my practice, I chose a really nice cream colored "parchment." This type of paper is often used by long-established law firms. I had it printed with black, raised letters and I think that it looked classy.

- Select an elegant paper.
- Don't skimp on the cost of paper.
- Avoid bright or strange colors.
- See the actual paper and "feel it" before printing.
- Print with raised lettering.
- Use a black script, but make sure that it is easy to read.
- Avoid logos; everyone else has them.
- Include company name, address, telephone and fax numbers, and web address.
- Print "second sheet" stationary with only your company name at ½ size

Other than your website, your stationary will be the first image most people will have of your company.

Business Cards

I used the same parchment as my letterhead.

Your business card should include the same information as your letterhead, plus your name, PE, title, and specialty.

> John F. Jones, PE, President
> Electrical Engineer

Company Brochure

During my second or third week in business, I went to a job site meeting with a mechanical engineer, who was also new in private practice. On the car seat, I found three pieces of paper stapled in the top left corner. It was his resume and a list of his projects. He proudly said, "That's my brochure." I didn't know anything about company brochures, but I knew that mine would be more "professional."

My "first" brochure was a resume and a three page list of past projects. It was enclosed in a thick blue 11 x 17 paper cover (folded in half) and printed with my letterhead and the words COMPANY BROCHURE in large letters.

My "second" brochure had padded black leather covers made by a "bookbinder." It had gold "embossed" lettering and included the name of the client (or potential client) also embossed on the cover. The pages were encased in plastic sleeves. Is anyone going to discard something with their name embossed prominently on the cover?

My "third" brochure was not as fancy, but it was more versatile. It was bound with flexible, glossy, and embossed black covers, and the pages were printed on my letterhead without sheet protectors. This was inserted in the front inside pocket of a 10 x 12 glossy folio. My company name was printed on the outside front of the folio, and my company description/resume was printed on the back. In the rear pocket of the folio, I inserted "fillers" that I had previously sent to my mailing list: published articles, award announcements, announcements of new services that our firm was offering, etc.

My "fourth" was a "mini-brochure": a single 8 ½ x 14 parchment sheet folded in thirds. It was only used as a handout at events, like speaking engagements with numerous attendees, when it was too expensive to provide my normal brochure. See Figure **9-1**.

Your brochure may evolve over time. But, most importantly, make it something of which you are "proud."

BROCHURE (1 OF 2)

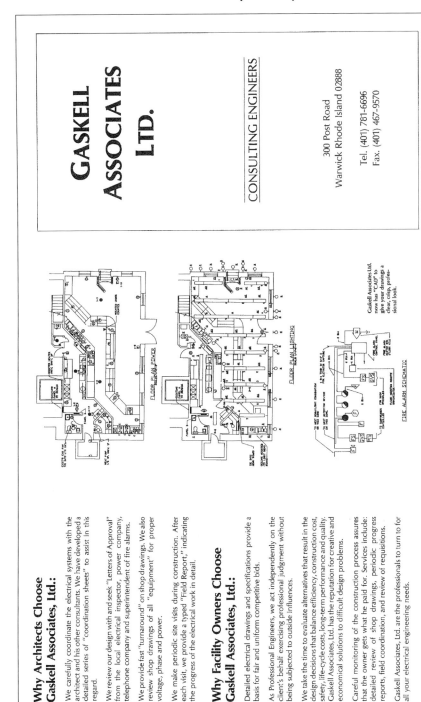

GASKELL ASSOCIATES LTD.

CONSULTING ENGINEERS

300 Post Road
Warwick Rhode Island 02888

Tel. (401) 781-6696
Fax. (401) 467-9570

FLOOR PLAN POWER

FLOOR PLAN LIGHTING

FIRE ALARM SCHEMATIC

Gaskell Associates Ltd. now has "CAD" to give your drawings a clear, crisp, professional look.

Why Architects Choose Gaskell Associates, Ltd.:

We carefully coordinate the electrical systems with the architect and his other consultants. We have developed a detailed series of "coordination sheets" to assist in this regard.

We review our design with and seek "Letters of Approval" from the local electrical inspector, power company, telephone company and superintendent of fire alarms.

We provide fast "turnaround" on shop drawings. We also review shop drawings of all "equipment" for proper voltage, phase and power.

We make periodic site visits during construction. After each visit, we provide a typed "Field Report," indicating the progress of the electrical work in detail.

Why Facility Owners Choose Gaskell Associates, Ltd.:

Detailed electrical drawings and specifications provide a basis for fair and uniform competitive bids.

As Professional Engineers, we act independently on the client's behalf exercising professional judgment without being subjected to outside influences.

We take the time to evaluate alternatives that result in the design decisions that balance efficiency, construction cost, safety, life-cycle costs, long-term performance and quality. Gaskell Associates, Ltd. has the reputation for creative and economical solutions to difficult design problems.

Careful monitoring of the construction process assures that the owner gets what he paid for. Services include: detailed review of shop drawings, periodic progress reports, field coordination, and review of requisitions.

Gaskell Associates, Ltd. are the professionals to turn to for all your electrical engineering needs.

FIGURE 9-1

BROCHURE (2 OF 2)

Gaskell Associates, Ltd.

Gaskell Associates, Ltd. is a consulting engineering firm primarily involved with the design of electrical systems for buildings.

Our specialties include:

- Power Distribution Systems
- Emergency Power Systems
- High Voltage Power Distribution Systems
- Lighting Design (Interior, Exterior, Area and Roadway)
- Fire Alarm Systems
- Burglar Alarm Systems
- Communications Systems
- MATV and CCTV Systems
- Computer Power and Network Systems
- UPS and Power Conditioning Systems
- Feasibility Studies

In addition, we have developed a team of consultants to allow us to offer a full range of incidental services including: HVAC, plumbing, architectural, structural, and civil engineering.

Life-cycle-costing is a major element of our design effort and energy conservation is always considered. This results in a facility that is economical, efficient, functional, and easily maintained, as well as one that is aesthetically pleasing.

Gaskell Associates, Ltd. endeavors, at all times, to maintain its reputation for accuracy, attention to detail, and punctuality. We have executed engineering projects for almost every type of facility, including numerous renovations.

This engineering practice was established in 1971 by John D. Gaskell, P.E., electrical engineer. We now employ a staff of eleven.

John D. Gaskell, P.E.

Gaskell Associates, Ltd. is headed by John D. Gaskell, P.E. Jack is a graduate of Wentworth Institute, with an Associates degree in Electrical Engineering Technology, and the University of Rhode Island, with a Bachelor of Science degree in Electrical Engineering. He is a Registered Professional Engineer in Rhode Island, Massachusetts, Connecticut, New Hampshire, New York, New Jersey, Pennsylvania, and Florida.

Jack is a member of the following professional organizations: Rhode Island Society of Professional Engineers, Providence Engineering Society, International Association of Electrical Inspectors, Electrical League of Rhode Island, Illuminating Engineering Society, and the Institute of Electrical and Electronic Engineers.

He is a past president of the Rhode Island Society of Professional Engineers; past president of the Rhode Island Chapter of the Illuminating Engineering Society, past director of the Electrical League of Rhode Island; and past director of the Rhode Island Chapter of the International Association of Electrical Inspectors.

Jack writes the electrical specifications for our projects and provides executive project management. He has written several articles for national technical publications. His design of a one megawatt Uninterruptible Power System for Fleet National Bank's Operations Center won "first place" in a national design award competition.

Jack was recently honored by being selected "Engineer of the Year" by the Rhode Island Society of Professional Engineers.

Recent Clients

a i designs, inc., Pawtucket, Rhode Island
Gordon R. Archibald, Inc., Pawtucket, Rhode Island
Arris Design, Inc., Providence, Rhode Island
James Barnes, AIA, Providence, Rhode Island
Benefit Street Design, Inc., Providence, Rhode Island
Brown University, Providence, Rhode Island
Citizens Bank, Properties Dept., Providence, Rhode Island
The Coken Company, Providence, Rhode Island
Corporate Concepts, Warwick, Rhode Island
Cranston Housing Authority, Cranston, Rhode Island
Daughn/Salisbury, Inc., Providence, Rhode Island
Diocese of Providence, Providence, Rhode Island
Di Leonardo International, Inc., Warwick, Rhode Island
East Providence Housing Authority, East Providence, Rhode Island
Ekman, Arp and Snider, Warwick, Rhode Island
Charles B. Fink, A.I.A., Providence, Rhode Island
Fleet National Bank, Properties Dept., Providence, Rhode Island
Carrollo Associates, Inc., Warwick, Rhode Island
Gates, Leighton & Associates, Inc., East Providence, Rhode Island
Gilbert & Maloney, Providence, Rhode Island
Irving B. Haynes & Associates, Providence, Rhode Island
The Hillier Group, Princeton, New Jersey
Kent Cruise & Partners, Providence, Rhode Island
Lamborghini and Felbelman, Providence, Rhode Island
Lincoln Housing Authority, Lincoln, Rhode Island
Long, Staats and Associates, Newport, Rhode Island
Americo Mallozzi, A.I.A., Providence, Rhode Island
George Morin Architects, Inc., Woonsocket, Rhode Island
Kevin S. Munroe – Architect, Wakefield, Rhode Island
Naval Underwater Systems Center, Newport, Rhode Island
O'Hearne Associates, Woonsocket, Rhode Island
Lee Pare & Associates, Inc., Providence, Rhode Island
City Of Pawtucket School Department, Pawtucket, Rhode Island
PPG Industries, Pittsburgh, Pennsylvania
Lombardi, Pozzi, A.I.A., Warren, Rhode Island
The Robinson Green Beretta Corp., (RGB), Providence, Rhode Island
Robinson, Myrick & Associates, Inc., Smithfield, Rhode Island
Roger Williams General Hospital, Providence, Rhode Island
The Ritchie Organization (TRO), Newton, Massachusetts
Rhode Island Department of Environmental Management
Rhode Island Department of Transportation
Rhode Island Division of Water Resources
Norton E. Salk, Architect, Cranston, Rhode Island
Raymond W. Schwab Associates, Inc., Peacedale, Rhode Island
St. Joseph Hospital, Fatima Unit, N. Providence, Rhode Island
St. Joseph Hospital, Providence Unit, Providence, Rhode Island
United States Navy, Newport, Rhode Island
Technical Materials, Inc., Lincoln, Rhode Island
Warren Housing Authority, Warren, Rhode Island
Warwick Housing Authority, Warwick, Rhode Island
City of Woonsocket, Planning Department, Woonsocket, RI
Womens Development Center, Providence, Rhode Island
Veteran's Medical Center, Providence, Rhode Island

FIGURE 9-1

Mailing List

When I first started my practice, all my clients were architects, and there were about 30 potential clients listed in the phone book's Yellow Pages. But by the end of my first year, my mailing list had expanded to over 500 names. I included all of the architects (even those who I didn't know or said they used someone else). Each time that I prepared a fee proposal for someone not on the list, I added them. In addition, I added the following:

- *Electrical Inspectors (People enquire: Who should I get to draw my electrical plans?)*
- *Electrical Supply Companies (Same question.)*
- *Electrical Contractors (Same question, plus they may hire your firm for design–build projects.)*
- *Housing Authorities (Director and facilities Manager.)*
- *Superintendents of Fire Alarms (People enquire: Who do I hire to design my fire alarm system?)*
- *Power Company Representatives (Plus, President and department heads.)*
- *Electrical Manufacturers Representatives (Many also call on architects.)*
- *Hospitals (Director of Facilities and President.)*
- *Universities (Director of Facilities and President.)*

Make your own list to suit your clients and industry. Your first mailing should be your business announcement.

I recommend a minimum of two mailings per year.

I used to send Thanksgivings cards; people notice them because they don't get many and it avoids a religious connotation associated with Christmas. My second mailing was often what I titled as an "update." It was always a single page (multiple pages don't get read), printed on my letterhead, and placed unfolded (easily filed) in a 9 x 12 envelope (it looks more important in a large envelope). I included mention of exciting projects, employee promotions, new services being offered, etc. Sometimes, my second mailing was a reprint of a magazine article about my projects or about a timely technical issue authored by me. See "Advanced Marketing Materials" later in this chapter.

Send all mailings to your entire mailing list, even if the contact may not be interested or may not be a potential client. They will remember you as an "expert" and recommend you.

I have had people question the value of an expanded mailing list, and I offer the following story:

I had a new client consisting of two partners. One wanted a "variance" (exception from a code requirement) regarding exit signs. The other said, "Don't waste your time, I applied for a variance three times on a previous project in that city, and they turned me down on all three." The client decided to apply anyway. So, he did the paper work and listed me as the electrical engineer. I had to go to the hearing with him (for free) to present our case.

At these hearings, cases are usually heard on a first-come, first-served basis; unfortunately, my client was at the last minute. As we entered the rear of the hearing room, the Variance Committee Chairman (whom I didn't know) was standing at the front and saw us enter. He said in a loud voice, "Welcome, Mr. Gaskell. We have a seat down here in the front for you. You can go first, and whatever you want, you get."

As it turned out, the chairman was a small (politically connected) electrical contractor whom I had never met, but who was on my mailing list and recognized me from my picture, which I included on many of my mailings. I'm not saying that this moment of recognition made my "self-promotion" all worthwhile, but it impressed this client and eventually gained me a nationwide reputation.

Follow this formula for promoting yourself and your firm and you will become the best-known engineer in your area.

Contact List

As you prepare your mailing list, complete a "contact form" for each person on the mailing list, and keep these forms in a 3-ring binder with dividers that match the categories on your mailing list. At the top of each sheet should be the same information as on the mailing label, plus telephone and fax numbers as well as e-mail address. Also, note company affiliation and any personal information, including how you met (if you have) and how you got his name. Use lined paper with a column on the left for the date of each contact.

The purpose of these contact forms is so you will remember when and how the person got on your mailing list. They may have called you for a fee proposal, you may have met them at an AIA meeting, or you may have gotten their name from the Yellow Pages. Each time that you make contact with the person, list the details on this sheet, including project names, if any. You may find a computer program to do all of this for you; the important thing is to have this information in some easily accessible form.

I recommend that you set aside one afternoon every 2 weeks to call your contacts. Tuesday, Wednesday, or Thursday afternoons between 1:30 and 4:30 are usually best. Regular clients you probably want to talk to once per month. For some, every 3 to 6 months is enough. Others, not at all. Make these calls brief. Start out by saying, "I'm just checking in to see how things are going."

Verify the status of each mutual current project with your project manager beforehand. If there are any unresolved issues, it might be best to postpone the call until they are resolved. Before you call, check your "accounts receivable list" so you know about overdue items. Ask about your mutual current projects.

Ask about upcoming projects. Try to get a verbal commitment. Offer to attend interviews, if appropriate. Try to get dates; your first project meeting will probably be several months after your client gets a contract. Get as much information as the client will share: project budget, square footage, likelihood of the project proceeding, etc. Make clear notes on the contact form. After the call, mark the date to follow up on your calendar.

Federal – Standard Form 330

In 2004, Standard Forms 254 and 255 were replaced with new Standard Form 330. This federal form helps agencies to assess qualifications of a professional design firm.

This form is available for download at www.gsa.gov. It is also used by some state and local government agencies in the hiring of architects and engineers. The instructions state:

> Federal agencies use this form to obtain information from architect-engineer (A-E) firms about their professional qualifications. Federal agencies select firms for A-E contracts on the basis of professional qualifications as required by the Brooks A-E Act (40 U.S.C. 1101 - 1104) and Part 36 of the Federal Acquisition Regulation (FAR).
>
> The Brooks A-E Act requires the public announcement of requirements for A-E services (with some exceptions provided by other statutes), and the selection of at least three of the most highly qualified firms based on demonstrated competence and professional qualifications according to specific criteria published in the announcement. The Act then requires the negotiation of a contract at a fair and reasonable price starting first with the most highly qualified firm.

The information used to evaluate firms is from this form and other sources, including performance evaluations, any additional data requested by the agency, and interviews with the most highly qualified firms and their references.

Part I presents the qualifications for a specific contract.

Part II presents the general qualifications of a firm or a specific branch office of a firm. Part II has two uses:

1. An A-E firm may submit Part II to the appropriate central, regional or local office of each Federal agency to be kept on file. A public announcement is not required for certain contracts, and agencies may use Part II as a basis for selecting at least three of the most highly qualified firms for discussions prior to requesting submission of Part I. Firms are encouraged to update Part II on file with agency offices, as appropriate, according to FAR Part 36. If a firm has branch offices, submit a separate Part II for each branch office seeking work.

2. Prepare a separate Part II for each firm that will be part of the team proposed for a specific contract and submitted with Part I. If a firm has branch offices, submit a separate Part II for each branch office that has a key role on the team.

It is important that you become familiar with this form and (as soon as you have established your practice) submit Part ll to appropriate agencies. I recommend that you find out who the contracting officers are in your area and contact them personally. Here is where your non-competitor consulting engineer friends can help.

In Rhode Island, my federal contacts included the following:

- *The VA Medical Center – Where I did upgrades to their 12.5 KV electric service, fire alarm upgrades, emergency power upgrades, and renovations to various areas.*
- *The US Naval Base in Newport – We often had an "area contract" which allowed them to negotiate a series of small contracts with us, usually for a one year period.*
- *Quonset Naval Air Station – Several projects.*

These contacts included contracting officers, project managers, and the chief engineers.

Selected Bidder List

This is an <u>important</u> tool in gaining favor with your trade contractors and in avoiding problems during construction. Prepare a "selected bidder list": the names and contact information of contractors of your specialty who do good work. Include only those who don't waste your time by submitting inferior shop drawings, don't chase *extras* (payment for things not called for on the drawings and specifications but clearly understood as being required), and who cooperate well during construction.

At the "final review meeting" with my private clients, I provide a copy of this list and recommend that only these bidders be invited to bid. I explain that these are, in my experience, THE BEST; they do great work, are easy to work with, use quality materials, and don't chase extras. My clients usually agree. I also tell them that during bidding, you will get calls from other contractors wanting to bid. Don't give in to them or we will both have a lot of grief and aggravation, including extra costs during construction. I also ask, "Can I assure these contractors that their bid will be handled ethically, the contract will be awarded to the low bidder, and you will not shop around for a lower price?"

Your architectural clients will usually not allow you to restrict bids on their projects. But it is a good idea to call your "selected bidder list" and inform them of the project; the more friendly bidders, the better.

ADVANCED MARKETING MATERIALS

From the Desk of

Print note paper (4 x 6) with "From the desk of: John J. Jones, PE, President," your company name, and your contact information at the bottom. Also, have some printed for your senior staff. It should be on the same paper as your letterhead. Attach it to anything that you mail to a client. It is much more "classy" than a blank piece of paper or a notepaper with a vendors name on it. A personal, handwritten note on nice paper makes the right impression.

The more prevalent use of internet communications has made note paper less relevant and important. However, a handwritten note gets more attention and may be more appropriate for certain interactions.

Pens

Pens with your company name provide a reminder of your company name and easy access to your telephone number. But everyone is giving out pens, and as soon as the ink wares out, it gets thrown away. If you do give out pens, buy a $2.00 pen, not the 20 cent kind.

Tape Measures

This was one of my best ideas. When reviewing a promotional catalog, I saw a tape measure with a window shade manufacture's name on it. In the construction industry, we most often deal with plans at ⅛ or ¼ scale. At meetings, architects often carry long scales (rulers) to measure distances. I had tape measures made with ¼ scale on one side of the tape and ⅛ scale on the other side. They were chrome with a black plastic insert including our company name (in the same script as our letterhead). They each came in a nice box (like for a piece of jewelry). I mailed them (in a small insulated mailing envelope) to anyone on my mailing list that might use one.

Each year, I had my secretary contact the local "Board of Registration for Architects" and request a list of those who passed the exam that year, including their addresses and registration numbers. I then sent the local newly registered architects a tape measure engraved with their name and registration number. I enclosed a note of congratulations on my "From the desk of" notepaper. I resisted the temptation of including any advertising literature.

In some cases, this was "long-term prospecting"; some new clients showed me one of my worn, 20-year-old tape measures.

Reprints of Articles

During my second or third year in business, power companies started to reduce their voltage to conserve energy. Clients became concerned that this might have a deleterious effect on their motors, lights, and electrical systems. I did some reading of textbooks and handbooks, made some calculations to quantify the results, and included this information in an update newsletter. It got rave reviews, so I expanded this information into a magazine article that actually got published. I ordered 1,000 reprints from the magazine and sent some of them to my mailing list. I used the extras as filler to my brochure. Overnight, I was thought to be an "expert."

You, too, can gain a reputation as an "expert." I recommend the following to get published:

- Select the most popular magazine in your industry, the one that engineers, contractors, and inspectors read.
- Review your project list, and select your most interesting recent project. Those that are appealing to magazine editors are prominent or use methods, materials, or techniques that are new or unusual.
- Alternatively, write about a timely issue in your industry. But first read the last 12 issues of the magazine to be sure that this topic has not already been exhaustively reviewed. If you can relate the topic to one or more of your projects, your chances of publication are improved.
- If your article mentions a project, you must verify that your client and the building owner/developer will not object to the mention of their project. An e-mail response is a good thing to have in your records. *One of my published articles was about an interesting generator upgrade at a local federal government facility. I later included a "reprint" when applying for another project at the same facility. I received a "cease and desist" letter from the contracting officer, and, in spite of my profuse apology, I didn't get another project at the facility for a couple of years.* Most clients are delighted, but don't skip this step, and don't wait until after you have spent a lot of time writing the article.
- Study previous articles, and format your article to match the magazine.
- Include many pictures with captions; you should be in some of them.
- Include a "headshot" photo of yourself.
- Include a brief biography (the same length as normally used in the magazine).
- Include sketches and 1-line diagrams, if appropriate.
- Call the magazine editor. Introduce yourself, and tell him a little about yourself and your submission. Ask to whom you should address the submission, and obtain both the e-mail address and the mailing address.
- Don't submit the same article to another publication unless you receive a rejection, but don't get discouraged. This is still a great promotional idea, even if the circulation of the magazine that accepts your article is smaller than your neighborhood; reprints are the key.

I recommend the following regarding reprints:

- Contact the publication. They usually have a third party who handles reprints.

- Design your reprint:
  - If possible, it should all be "one piece" (single fold – 4 printable surfaces, or two fold – 6 printable surfaces).
  - The first page should be the cover of the issue (delete extraneous items and the date to avoid limiting future use).
  - The following pages are your article (delete advertisements and extraneous items).
  - The last page should be your company description.
  - If you have an extra page, make the blank page your last, but print your company name, address, etc. at the bottom. If the article introduces a new company service, reprint the announcement here.
- Use "glossy" paper.
- Print in "black and white"; color is too expensive.
- Print enough copies for your initial mailing plus "stuffers" for your brochure.

The following are several examples:

- Article about one of our projects, "Upgradable Power Conditioning Unit Serves Law Firm," by the Senior Editor of Electrical Construction & Maintenance (EC&M) magazine. It was 11 x 17 and folded in half. I added our company name to the front cover and deleted distracting information. Also, I deleted the publication date to extend the usage of these reprints.
- Article about one of our projects and technical information on the problem that we solved, "Power Factor Improvement Provides Multiple Benefits, by the Senior Editor of EC&M. It was two pieces: 11 x 17 outer folded cover with an 8 ½ x 11 insert.
- Article about a technical issue, "Electrical Design with EMF in Mind," written by me and published in EC&M. It was 11 x 17 folded sheet. See Figure **9-2.**
- Article about one of our projects and technical information on the problem that we solved, "Expandable UPS Serves Bank Operations Center," written by me and published in EC&M. It was two 11 x 17 sheets folded and stapled on the fold. I finally got smart and added information to the back cover: me, my firm, and the technical issue addressed in my article.

- Article about a problem that I solved, "Anatomy of a Power Outage," written by me and published in EC&M. It was an 11 x 17 folded sheet.
- Article about a technical issue, "Avoiding EMFs – Designing Buildings Limiting Occupants Exposure to EMFs," written by me and published in EC&M. It was two pieces: 11 x 17 outer folded cover with an 8 ½ x 11 insert. I added my resume on the last page. It was this article that gained me the notoriety that resulted in my being invited to speak at the National Conference on Harmonics & Power Quality in Philadelphia, PA.

ELECTRICAL CONSTRUCTION AND MAINTENANCE

Electrical Design With EMF In Mind

What are electromagnetic fields and what efforts
should be made to minimize them in designing
electrical systems today?

**ELECTRICAL ENGINEERING BY
GASKELL ASSOCIATES, LTD.
CONSULTING ENGINEERS**

FIGURE 9-2

WHAT'S THE STORY

Electrical Design With EMF In Mind

What are electromagnetic fields and what efforts should be made to minimize them in designing electrical systems today?

John D. Gaskell, P.E.
John D. Gaskell, P.E. is President of Gaskell Associates, Ltd., a consulting engineering firm in Warwick, R.I., and a member of the National Electromagnetic Field Testing Association.

While it may be years before a clear consensus is established on the health risks of electromagnetic fields (EMF) exposure, the topic remains highly controversial. In the meantime, electrical systems can be designed and installed to minimize the extent of the magnetic field component of EMF, often at little or no added cost. Before discussing the steps that can be taken during the design stages of electrical distribution systems, let's find out what EMF is.

What is EMF?

EMF at 60Hz is really made up of two separate entities: electric fields and magnetic fields. An *electric* field, which exists when voltage is present and which is easily blocked by metal, can cause currents to flow on the *surface* of the human body. Electric fields are *not* generally considered to be a biological hazard.

A *magnetic* field, which exists when current flows and which is *not* appreciably blocked by common materials, can cause current to flow *through* the human body. Magnetic fields at 60 Hz *are* considered a possible biological hazard.

A magnetic field decreases as the distance from the source increases. However, the configuration of the source actually determines how quickly a field diminishes. Multiple conductors with current flowing in opposite directions or 3-phase circuits have magnetic fields that are inversely proportional to the distance *squared*. Appliances and transformers are point sources and their fields drops off inversely proportional to the distance *cubed*.

Exposure factors

Without consensus in the scientific community that a hazard actually exists, economics play a big factor in setting limits. We don't know for sure whether long-term, low-level exposure is worse than short-term, high-level exposure.

Some say that switched fields are more dangerous than steady-state fields. Individual characteristics of the person being exposed may need to be considered; age, health, and even fertility and pregnancy may be factors. Obviously, more research is needed. But in the meantime, it may be practical to make some educated guesses, set some *interim* exposure limits, and consider some changes in design.

Practical design suggestions

Services. For an overhead MV service lateral, consider selecting spacer cable in lieu of cross-arm construction. Utilities are becoming more sensitive to the magnetic field issue and may welcome your suggestions. Another choice for a service lateral, of course, is an underground service.

Preferably, pass a service lateral under a storage room rather than an office that is occupied for long time periods. If this cannot be done, then the service lateral should be enclosed in a metallic raceway. The magnetic field will induce a counter EMF in the metallic raceway, which will help reduce the field.

Locate pad-mounted transformers at least 20 ft from buildings. Another consideration is to encircle a pad-mounted trans-

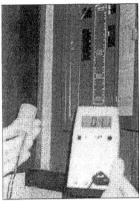

A magnetic field meter assembly consists of a digital multimeter, modified for additional shielding, and a magnetic sensor.

former with a fence, located at a 4- to 6-ft distance from the edge of the pad.

Switchboards and panels. Locate distribution equipment on exterior walls or walls adjacent to storage areas or corridors. Where possible, locate free-standing switchboards to allow 3 ft of working space on all sides. Use walls abutting occupied spaces for telephone or fire alarm equipment. Avoid locating an electrical room directly below or above an occupied space.

Indoor transformers. Although a typical dry-type, step-down power transformer creates a large magnetic field, this field's strength dissipates very quickly. However, it would still be good practice to locate such a unit in an electrical room remote from occupied spaces.

Bus duct. For vertical distribution of power in a tall building, follow a procedure similar to an indoor transformer siting. Where possible, run a vertical bus duct on a wall common to the elevator shaft, janitor closet, or corridor. In a factory, a bus duct run should be located away from operator positions.

Underfloor ducts. Individual conductors are usually installed in an underfloor duct system, and it is possible for the phase and

EC&M February 1995

FIGURE 9-2

120

EC&M ARTICLE (3 OF 3)

neutral conductors of a 2-wire branch circuit to be from 6 to 23 in. apart (depending on the cross section of the cell). This configuration would create significant magnetic fields. Recommended practice would be to twist the individual conductors of a branch circuit together in pairs. For a large new construction project, twisted cable assemblies can be purchased from specialty cable companies with only a slight increase in cost. At an existing installation, all the wires in the duct could be tie-wrapped at each outlet in the duct system.

What to watch out for

Wiring errors. When conductors are installed in such a way that circuit conductors are not in the same cable or raceway, substantial magnetic fields are created by the separated supply and return currents. The most common error is violating Sec. 250-23(a) by making a connection between a neutral and an equipment grounding conductor on the load side of the service disconnect; this usually happens at sub-panels. In this instance, neutral currents will flow on *both* the neutral and the equipment grounding conductor.

Other errors include incorrect wiring of 3-way switching circuits and the connection of neutrals from two different branch circuits at some point other than panel neutral busses, such as at junction boxes, switches, receptacles, etc.

Water pipe problems. Three specific areas can be addressed here.

• Neutral grounds to a water pipe on the load side of the service can cause problems similar to the case mentioned above, where Sec. 250-23(a) is violated by making a connection between a neutral and an equipment grounding conductor, on the load side of the service disconnect. If any electrical equipment, such as a hot water heater, is also connected to a metal water pipe, the water pipe will probably become a parallel path for current that should be flowing over the neutral.

• Physical damage or corrosion can cause the neutral conductor (often uninsulated) on an overhead service drop to open up, or sever. With this condition and with water supply laterals connected to conductive water mains, the water system can function as a parallel neutral. When this happens, unbalanced neutral currents seeking to return to the utility source will pass out of the building over the water lateral. They will return to the source after passing through the water main, a neigh-

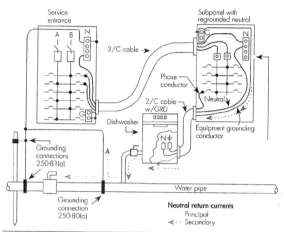

An example of a connection that allows a water pipe to function as a parallel neutral. The equipment grounding conductor run to the neutral bus of the subpanel is a violation of the NEC. This type of wiring error is widespread.

boring water lateral, and then through the neighboring service disconnect and out over the neighboring neutral.

• Currents can originate outside a building from the power company distribution system (typically, a looped primary circuit) or from neighboring buildings via the water service. An insulating coupling, or fitting, can be installed in the water service. However, it must be located *outside* of the premises, at least 10 ft from the building wall, per NEC Sec. 250-81(a).

Note that installing an insulating fitting in a water line to prevent the entry of currents has the disadvantage of decreasing ground conductivity, which under certain fault conditions may cause excess voltage to appear on plumbing fixtures and appliance enclosures. Thus, an insulating fitting can cause both a shock hazard and damage to an appliance that would not have occurred if there had been a connection to the water system.

However, a device called an automatic ground connector, which reconnects the ground in the event of a severe fault, is available. This device is similar in principle to a conventional surge arrester, but operates on a different voltage range. Because this is a new device that has not yet been tested by a recognized testing authority, approval from the local au-

thority having jurisdiction should be obtained.

When an insulating fitting is installed, a ground wire should be clamped beyond the fitting and extended back into the building. This allows the option of installing an automatic ground connector or reestablishing the ground in the future.

The importance of testing

Conducting a magnetic field survey upon completion of an installation in new construction is recommended. Such a survey can be done also at an existing location to detect long standing wiring errors or other abnormal conditions.

Two different types of meters are used. A single coil, or single axis, meter (about $235) determines the direction of the field and is useful for finding the field source. This type of meter can provide an approximate rms reading, but a calculation is required.

A 3-coil or 3-axis meter (about $1400) gives a true rms reading of fields from all directions and is not dependent on the orientation of the meter. Capable of making readings every 4 sec over a 24-hr period, this type of meter can be left at a site, or a person can carry it along a predetermined path. Accumulated data can be downloaded into a computer.   •

FIGURE 9-2

Award Announcements

Anytime someone in your firm receives a noteworthy award, send out an announcement.

The following are several examples:

- Announcement of award, "I.E.S. Lighting Design Award for the Hall Library Lighting Design," by the New England Section of IES. See Figure **9-3.**
- Announcement of award, "I.E.S. Lighting Design Award for the Lincoln School Gymnasium," by the Rhode Island Chapter of IES. Interestingly, both this and the previous project were submitted to the awards committee of the New England Section for their "Annual Awards," but only one was selected. Once the RI Chapter heard about the rejection, they decided to give us an award, even though they didn't host a contest. The fact that I was the Founding President of the RI Chapter may have had something to do with it, but I didn't request it.
- Announcement of award, "What it takes to Achieve Excellence in Systems Design," by Electrical Systems Design Magazine. I reprinted the magazine article without mention of the other four winners.

Don't sit by the phone waiting for a call from someone saying that "You have been selected to receive the Hale-Fellow-Well-Met Award." Awards don't just arrive; they come because "You make them happen."

You will remember, under "Getting Known & Gaining Credentials" in Chapter 2, I explained how to become president of an engineering society and how to receive their top award. These would both be good opportunities for an "award announcement," if they occurred recently. Also, you don't necessarily need to become an officer of an organization to receive an award. If you become active in the organization, with a little effort, you can usually find someone to nominate you and lobby for the votes needed.

When I sold my engineering firm, I stayed on to help our new division get established. We hired a capable new Division Director. However, he had never joined any engineering societies and had received few awards. I nominated him for the "Young Engineer of the Year" Award given by a local engineering society. I signed my nomination letter "Past President." I also contacted four other past presidents, who sent letters. I then called the current president and the awards chairmen to lobby for my nominee. In addition, our new Division Director had three "Letters of Reference" submitted to the awards chairmen. The Awards Banquet was the first meeting of this group that our Division Director had ever attended. Our company sponsored a table, and I arranged for someone to take plenty of pictures.

A glossy color announcement was printed and sent to our mailing list, and extra copies were saved to be used as filler. Also, a (free) announcement was made along with a picture in the "geek" section of the Sunday newspaper.

Things don't just happen; you make them happen.

AWARD ANNOUNCEMENT

I.E.S. AWARD PRESENTED
FOR HALL LIBRARY LIGHTING DESIGN

The restoration of the Hall Library in Cranston, Rhode Island called for a complete lighting upgrade to assure footcandle levels consistent with modern standards. In keeping with the historic nature of the building, existing fixtures were retrofitted with high lumen H.I.D. sources and supplemented with additional luminairs to produce award winning results.

Architect	The Robinson Green Beretta Corp.
Architectural Project Manager	Frederik R. Love, A.I.A.
Electrical Project Manager	Jefferey L. Clymer

Jack Gaskell, President of Gaskell Associates, Ltd. with Jeff Clymer, Project Manager at IESNA New England Section Awards Dinner.

Chain-hung globe-type fixtures were retrofitted to metal halide and supplemented with new recessed metal halide down lights.

False skylite was back lighted by indirect metal halide floods. Half inch parabolic cubed louvers control glare from fluorescent fixtures at main desk.

Fluorescent fixtures provide excellent vertical footcandle levels on book stacks. Up-light from globes highlight the hand carved wood moldings.

GASKELL ASSOCIATES, LTD. *CONSULTING ENGINEERS*
300 Post Road, Warwick, RI 02888 (401) 781-6696

FIGURE 9-3

Announcements of New Services or New Specialties

What is a New Service or New Specialty? Well, it depends upon the type of engineering that you do.

See OFFER SPECIALIZED SERVICES in Chapter 10.

Whenever you start a new service or new specialty, send out an announcement. The following is an example:

- Announcement of new service, "Power Quality Monitoring." See Figure **9-4.**

As stated previously, send these to your mailing list and have extra copies made to be used as brochure filler. Also, place a (free) announcement along with a picture in the local Sunday newspaper. Also, send it to related organizations and suggest that they make mention of it in their newsletters.

ANNOUNCEMENT OF NEW SERVICE (1 OF 2)

Power Quality Monitoring

SINE WAVE   TRANSIENT   NOTCH

SWELL   SAG   WAVE SHAPE FAULT

POWER QUALITY MONITORING & CERTIFICATION SERVICES

a division of

GASKELL ASSOCIATES, LTD.

Consulting Electrical Engineers

300 POST ROAD
WARWICK RHODE ISLAND 02888

Tel. (401) 781-6696
Fax (401) 467-9570
Toll Free (888) 781-6696

Call Today

Our service is intended to save money by extending equipment life and improving the reliability of the equipment and facility that your business depends upon.

The fee for our services depends upon the sophistication of the equipment we provide and the complexity and frequency of reports that you require.

We will be happy to customize a no obligation quotation for our services to suit your facility, match your needs, and meet your budget.

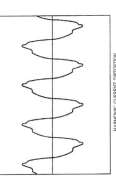

HARMONIC CURRENT DISTORTION

Power Quality Monitoring and Certification Service is a subsidiary of Gaskell Associates, Ltd. Electrical Consulting Engineers. Established in 1971, they are the largest electrical engineering firm in Rhode Island.

Gaskell Associates, Ltd. is headed by John D. Gaskell, P.E. Jack is a graduate of the University of Rhode Island, with a Bachelor of Science degree in Electrical Engineering. He is a Registered Professional Engineer in Rhode Island, Massachusetts, Connecticut, New York, New Jersey, and New Hampshire.

Jack is a member of the following professional organizations: Rhode Island Society of Professional Engineers, Providence Engineering Society, Electrical League of Rhode Island, Illuminating Engineering Society, National Electromagnetic Field Testing Association, National Forensic Center, and the National Academy of Forensic Engineers.

He is past President of the Rhode Island Society of Professional Engineers and a past President of the Rhode Island Chapter of the Illuminating Engineering Society. Jack is currently a Director of the Electrical League of Rhode Island and is a member of both the Engineering Advisory Board and the Corporation of Roger Williams University. He is also a member of the Rhode Island Building Codes Standards Committee.

Jack has written numerous articles for national technical publications and has been a guest speaker at the National Conference on Harmonics and Power Quality. He is a nationally recognized expert on magnetic fields. Jack was recently honored by being selected "Engineer of the Year" by the Rhode Island Society of Professional Engineers and is recipient of the Providence Engineering Society's "Freeman Award" for advancement in the art and practice of engineering.

FIGURE 9-4

ANNOUNCEMENT OF NEW SERVICE (2 OF 2)

Summary:

For a small monthly fee, **"Power Quality Monitoring & Certification Services"** will provide equipment to continuously monitor power quality at your facility and provide periodic reports summarizing and analyzing data recorded. Detecting and correcting power quality problems early may avoid damage to equipment or loss of critical data. Proof of acceptable power quality, (certified by a **Professional Engineer**) may prevent "voiding" of your equipment warranties/guarantees. Proof that power anomalies originated on the power company system may qualify you for reimbursement if damage occurs.

Our Service Offers
Two Unique Advantages:

1. There is no need for you to purchase equipment, pay for installation and wiring, or hire a specialist to interpret the recordings.

2. Our reports are "certified" by a licensed, experienced, independent **Professional Engineer***.

*Note: John D. Gaskell, P.E. is a Registered Professional Engineer in RI, MA, CT, NH, NY, & NJ

How This Service Works:

Basically, our power quality monitoring service works as follows:

We install one or more sophisticated power quality monitors at your facility. There is no cost to you for equipment, installation* and associated wiring and maintenance. (*Note: Beyond 100 miles from R.I., there is a small one-time installation charge).

Monitoring capabilities depend upon the "LEVEL" of the equipment installed. Level I equipment will continuously monitor and periodically record current and voltage on all phases and neutral, as well as voltage between neutral and ground. In addition, it will detect and record the following power anomalies:

•Transients   •Overvoltages
•Sags   •Undervoltages
•Swells   •Interruptions

We provide a telephone modem and connect to a telephone line which you extend to the vicinity of each meter and assign for our use. We periodically call your facility and download the data recorded.

We prepare reports (usually monthly) which summarize and analyze the data accumulated.

Why Your Facility Should Be Monitored.

Facilities now have computer based loads that are more sensitive to the imperfections that have always existed in the power supplied to them. Power aberrations can cause reduced equipment/component life, software damage, memory loss, equipment failures and power outages. With power company deregulation and associated cost cutting, many business owners are concerned that they will be unaware of a decline in power quality, until damage has already occurred.

Our reports, certified by a **Professional Engineer**, usually provide proof that your power quality for the period was within industry accepted tolerances. This proof may prevent your equipment suppliers from *Voiding Equipment Guarantees/Warranties*, based on claims of poor power quality or acts of God: e.g. lightning.

If a power quality event occurs that exceeds "industry standards" (or exceeds limits that you define), our report will notify you of the event and describe the likely causes. This will allow you to take remedial action in a timely manner and possibly avoid damage to your equipment or facility, or prevent loss of critical data.

The report will include the date, time, and type of each power quality event. Depending upon the "level" of monitoring that you choose, it will usually indicate the direction of the event so that you will know if it occurred on the power company system or within your facility. This information could be particularly important if the event resulted in damage.

FIGURE 9-4

Other Ideas

Anniversary Stickers

Every 10 years, put stickers on all of your correspondence: 10th Anniversary, 20th Anniversary, 30th Anniversary. Fancy gold or silver embossed stickers with your company name are available and inexpensive. Use them for the entire anniversary year. *I have a friend who, in addition to being a professional engineer, is also a registered land surveyor and owned a firm that had been in business for over 100 years. Not many businesses survive the first 10 years; 100 years is impressive, to say the least.* Make a big deal about your anniversary every 10 years.

Post Cards

When we first started using Auto-CAD, I sent out post cards to those on my mailing list. It had a picture of our new plotter with a large sheet hanging out that said, "Gaskell Associates now has CAD to better serve our clients." There was no message, only the picture.

With a little creativity, you can come up with other ideas.

OUTLINE SUMMARY

- **Business announcement:** Make your business announcement outstanding. It should look like a wedding invitation on fine thick paper with raised letters.

- **Letterhead & business cards:** Create elegant letterhead and business cards. Parchment with raised letters and no logo would be a good choice.

- **Brochure:** Your brochure is the face of the company. It will evolve as your firm grows. Try to make it versatile and something that will make you proud and distinguish you from your competitors.

- **Mailing list:** Your mailing list is one of your most important promotional tools. Expand it to include those who may recommend you. Send all mailings to the entire list. Send a minimum of two per year, including updates, announcements, and holiday cards.

- **Lists & forms:** Create the lists and forms that your firm needs. Expand your contact list, prepare your government 330 form, and avoid construction headaches with your selected bidder list.

- **Promotional items:** Don't overlook personalized note paper, post cards, pens, tape measures, and anniversary stickers.

- **Articles:** Write and publish technical articles, send reprints to your mailing list, and include them with your brochure. Everyone will consider you to be an "expert" in your field.

- **Announcements:** Don't forget to send out announcements of awards, new services/specialties, and anniversaries.

CHAPTER 10

MARKETING METHODS

INTRODUCTION

You will discover both what to do and not do when marketing your new consulting engineering firm. Find out how easy it is to get leads and referrals. Understand which other potential clients are seeking your services, besides architects. See how developing a new "specialty" generates work for which you don't need to *compete*. Realize how public speaking opportunities are *free* publicity. Learn how entertaining clients and potential clients will garner loyalty. Ascertain why notes of congratulations and thanks and an occasional party will help your practice grow.

YOUR INITIAL PROJECTS

When you were creating your Business Plan, you did a Cash Inflow Projection (as described in Chapter 4 –Financial Forecasting). In estimating your income, you prepared a list of existing and potential clients and made some initial contacts to determine if you could count on their business. Have your notes from those meetings in hand when you contact them again. You need to start looking for work as soon as you have cast off (see Chapter 7).

Recontact those who indicated that they "would" give you work, those who said they "may," and even those who were "unsure." Tell them the good news and the date of your office opening. Be positive and upbeat. Ask what projects you can immediately start on. Also, ask about future projects and associated expected start dates. Try to get a commitment. I recommend meeting in person with your best prospects. For those who said they "may" and those who were "unsure," I would drop by without an appointment "to drop-off a brochure" rather than risk getting *shot down* over the phone.

WARNING: Do no not "stamp" (seal) any documents until you have "professional liability insurance" (Errors & Omissions). See Chapter 8.

YOUR WEBSITE

Much to my surprise, an engineering firm's website has become one of the most active sources of new clients. Some new clients will go to your website because of a referral or because they have heard that a competitor of theirs does business with your firm. However, you will find that many of your clients will find you while surfing the net.

First of all, your website should look professional. Do not try to design it yourself; hire an experienced professional. If you have a colleague who has a great website, ask about his website designer. Did the designer heed the client's wishes, and was working with him/her easy? Were they prompt in constructing the site and in making requested updates? How are the hosting services?

Your website should have the following general features: be quick and easy to navigate, not produce any sound/audio, bear the same main headings on each page, be easily changed and updated, and have no blinking, spinning, or moving parts. The site should be automatically backed up and integrated with Facebook, Twitter, and other social media.

Search engine optimization (SEO) is the process of affecting the visibility of a website in a search engine's unpaid search results. In general, the earlier (or higher ranked on the search results page) and more frequently a site appears in the search results list, the more visitors it will receive from the search engine's users.

This Internet marketing strategy considers how search engines work, what people search for, the actual search terms or keywords typed into search engines, and which search engines are preferred by their targeted audience. Optimizing a website may involve editing its content and associated coding to both increase its relevance to specific keywords and remove barriers to the indexing activities of search engines. Promoting a site to increase the number of backlinks, or inbound links, is another tactic.

Often, your website designer is experienced in SEO. Make sure that whomever you choose is ethical. While SEOs can provide clients with valuable services, some unethical SEOs have given the industry a black eye through their overly aggressive marketing efforts and their attempts to manipulate search engine results in unfair ways. Practices that violate search engine guidelines may result in a negative adjustment of your site's presence or even the removal of your site from the index.

Website ads are a way to drive traffic to your website. However, I believe that your money would be better spent on an attractive website and better SEO.

CLIENTS

A client (obviously) is anyone who pays you for engineering services. I call clients who operate an "Architectural Practice" ARCHITECTURAL CLIENTS.

I call all other clients PRIVATE CLIENTS (even though some of them may be graduate architects). They include hospitals, colleges/universities, federal agencies, housing authorities, electrical contractors, attorneys/law firms, and many others.

SEARCHING FOR NEW ARCHITECTURAL CLIENTS

Contacts

Hopefully, you are busy with new work, but now is the time to promote work from new sources. Expand your list of potential clients to include those whom you have not worked with in the past. First, look thru the list of contacts that you have acquired since you started working, both in the course of business and in your work with engineering societies. Those whom you have impressed are often willing to introduce you to potential clients.

Networking

Continue attending some of the meetings of the engineering and industry societies to which you belong. Hopefully, you have already done your turn on these boards because your time will be limited while planning and starting a new practice.

If you haven't already, also become an associate/affiliate member of the local chapter of the American Institute of Architects (AIA) and attend some meetings. There, you will see some of your new clients, who may introduce you to potential clients. However, you will find that sitting through lectures on windows and doors is mind numbing.

The construction industry usually has one or more golf leagues. This may produce some business, but don't let it take up too much of your time.

Consulting Engineers

Consulting engineers of a different "specialty" are often willing to share clients. *I often got good leads from mechanical engineers, civil engineers, and structural engineers. They frequently provided firm names and contact information as well as names of upcoming projects. We were not competitors, and I reciprocated when I could.*

Land Surveyors

Land surveyors often find out about proposed projects even before an architect is selected. Making friends with them and periodically contacting them can provide good leads. Passing this information along to your architectural clients who specialize in the type of project planned can pay off for this and future projects. Knowing each of your client's specialties is important.

Search the Internet

It is not hard to come up with a list of local architects, but many are moon-lighters who do only small houses and, therefore, are not potential clients (at least for now). Some listed are actually contractors and, also, not potential architectural clients. Other consultants, salesmen, and existing clients can help you identify the "players."

Newspapers

Upcoming major projects are often mentioned in "news" items in your local newspapers. If the architect is mentioned, give him a call. Express congratulations and ask if your specialty is not yet committed. If already pledged, ask about other projects coming up.

If the architect is not identified in the article, get his name from the project contractor, developer, local building inspector, mayor's office, or Chamber of Commerce.

Another source of leads is the classifieds. Government agencies publish "Requests for Proposals" (RFPs) for architect and engineers for most upcoming projects. Most of them are for architectural services. Most architects are "generalists" and will pursue any kind of project. Others specialize in one or few types of projects (historic restoration, custom homes, libraries, housing authorities, etc.). Ahead of time, prepare an e-mail list for each of the most common categories of clients along with a standard message:

Attached is a recent RFP to which you may be interested in responding. If so, we would like to be part of your team. Attached is a copy of our company description, my resume, and a list of our related projects. Let me know if you need any additional information. As always, I am available to attend an interview with you.

Once you have this system set up, your secretary can do most of the work.

Construction Lead Services

Construction lead service companies provide leads for contractors. The F.W. Dodge Company is a subsidiary of the McGraw-Hill Company and is one of the largest. These services are expensive, and most leads relate to projects that are in the bidding phase and are too late for engineering services. But a friendly contractor may be willing to share appropriate leads with you.

SEARCHING FOR NEW PRIVATE CLIENTS

As mentioned previously, "private clients" are any clients who are not in an architectural practice. Many of the same sources mentioned above also apply to private clients.

Trade Contractors

Trade contractors are often asked by general contractors to bid on "design–build" projects, which include plans and specifications sealed by a professional engineer. These projects often require some missionary (unpaid) work upfront. My advice, if you are willing to take a risk, is don't donate more than 8 hours and get paid for an extra 40 hours if the project goes ahead. But BEWARE: contractors are notorious for "stiffing" engineers. However, you can usually trust the contractors on your Selected Bidders List because they are already somewhat beholden to you.

Housing Authorities

Housing authorities are great for upgrades (i.e., electrical, including fire alarm, generator, and lighting), but they usually hire architects for major renovations. Although, I had such a valued relationship with some housing authorities that they required their architects to hire me, and a few even separated the electrical engineering from the architect's contract and hired me directly. This work, of course, is subject to funding cuts.

Hospitals

These are critical facilities and the work is specialized. The same comments as above apply here. This can be some of your most profitable work; there is little competition, and the need for hospital work usually does not fluctuate with the economy.

Colleges & Universities

Higher educational facilities are recession-proof clients. The same comments as above apply here.

Federal Agencies

See "Standard Form 330" mentioned earlier in Chapter 9 – Marketing Materials.

FedBizOpps (FBO) Database

Effective January 1, 2002, the FedBizOpps (FBO) database has replaced the Commerce Business Daily (CBD). This new FBO/CBD database (found at fbo.gov) is identical to the old CBD format. This is an online electronic database that can be searched for federal government architect and engineer opportunities.

Again, once you have the search system method narrowed down, your secretary can do most of the work.

Attorneys/Law Firms

If you are confident, knowledgeable, and well-spoken, serving as an expert witness should be part of your engineering practice.

See Chapter 16 – Forensic Engineering.

OFFER SPECIALIZED SERVICES

What is a new specialty or new service? Well, it depends upon the type of engineering that you practice.

Our general specialty was the design of electrical systems for buildings. But we had many sub-specialties which we enumerated in our company brochure: lighting, electrical services, power distribution, fire alarm systems, emergency/stand-by power systems, uninterruptable power supply systems, etc. Also, if a potential client mentioned any kind of electrical system or building type, my response was always: "That's one of our specialties."

At various times in my career as an electrical consulting engineer, I offered the following new services:

Electromagnetic Field Investigations & Mitigation

A number of years back, EMFs (electromagnetic fields) were a "hot topic." Many people became concerned that the electromagnetic fields emitted by low frequency (60 cycle) power sources might cause serious health concerns. People were especially apprehensive about their proximity to high voltage power lines. Some people changed to wind-up alarm clocks rather than sleep with a small electric motor near their heads.

I bought a couple of "gauss" meters, took measurements, and did some studying. Then, I wrote an article that was published in a national magazine. I identified and quantified the sources; I left the health issues to others. I became a member of the National Electromagnetic Field Testing Association. Later, I was a guest speaker at "The National Conference on Harmonics & Power Quality in Philadelphia, PA." I was the go-to-guy for magnetic field projects. In office buildings and in universities, computer screens were distorted due to proximity to power sources. In data centers, computers were acting erratically for the same reason. My services would start with a study, including measuring and mapping the fields, recommending solutions, and estimating costs of mitigation. This was often followed by a design phase, bid phase, and construction observation phase. I didn't have any competition, and I was well paid for both my services and expertize.

Power Quality Services

Another "hot topic" was power quality. Basically, on a three-phase power system, each of the phases are separated 120 degrees from each other, which causes cancelation and results in very little neutral current. However, for computer loads, a "third harmonic current" can occur, causing the neutral current to exceed the phase currents. I, again, was considered an "expert" and did quite a number of power quality studies, and most included preparation of 1-line diagrams on an hourly basis. Again, no competition, well paid.

Uninterruptable Power Systems (UPS)

A UPS is a device consisting of a battery and an inverter to provide AC power to a load without interruption if commercial power fails. You can buy a small UPS at your local electronics store. You don't need an engineer to design the installation, just plug your computer into it, and no information is lost during a blackout.

However, systems for computer rooms are huge and complex and require engineering, including paralleling of units, backup generators, bypass for uninterrupted maintenance, and complicated cooling. After a large installation, I wrote a magazine article titled, "UPS Installation at Bank Data Center is expandable to 5 Megawatts." I was then considered the data center/UPS expert.

A few years later, a US manufacturer of small UPS units bought a Danish company that manufactured large units. They had the technical manuals and catalogs converted to English, but they were concerned because the result was what they called "Danglish." I wasn't sure what they wanted from me, but when they called, I went to meet with them. Two young guys met me in the reception area and took me to the cafeteria to discuss it over coffee. While I was giving my usual "spiel" to the 30-year-old manager, his 25-year-old assistant was thumbing through my brochure. First, the assistant interrupted to say, "There is an article here that he wrote about 'Power Quality.'" Next, he said, "He also wrote an article about a UPS System that he designed."

At this point, the manager held up his hand to stop me from talking and said, "We have done a nationwide search, and yours is the only name that has come up more than once. We don't know what you are going to charge, but you're the guy we want."

This was a very unusual assignment; it was not an engineering design. I gave them two proposals:

The first proposal was to rewrite the "text" of the catalog, rewrite the "white papers," and explain how to reorganize the catalog to be more user friendly for consulting engineers. I was also specific on the number of review meetings.

The second proposal (which they hadn't asked for) was for me to be available for "telephone consultations" for up to 8 hours per month for a monthly fee. This was a whole new area of business for them, and they were not used to marketing their product to consulting engineers and also to data center managers. I didn't work for cheap, but I restrained myself from overcharging.

They accepted both proposals. After three months with no telephone consultations, I started to spend a few hours each month reviewing catalog material of their competitors and industry magazines. I sent them e-mails with suggestions for new related products and services. They were happy with the catalog work and continued my monthly fee for over a year. They also became a client for numerous UPS and data center designs as well as some upgrades at their various manufacturing facilities.

Arc Flash Calculations

More recently, another "hot topic" called "arc flash" became a concern. Since the days of Thomas Edison, the largest electrical concern has been "short-circuits": the <u>high</u>

inrush of current when two opposite polarity electrical wires touch. A newer concern is "arc flash": the *heat and flash* associated with the same event. (Google "arc flash" for some gruesome videos.)

I, again, became considered an "expert" and did quite a number of arc flash studies, and most included preparation of 1-line diagrams, fault current calculations, and panel labeling on an hourly basis. Again, no competition (at the time), and well paid.

Look around for an opportunity to become an "expert" on a current topic and the chance to offer a new service with little competition and unrestrained fees.

PUBLIC SPEAKING OPPORTUNITIES

Almost any kind of speaking engagement enhances your image and credibility.

Teaching

Most professional organizations offer continuing education courses. It will enhance your reputation to arrange to be a guest lecturer.

The RI Chapter of the Illuminating Engineering Society every couple of years offered either a Basic Lighting Course or an Advanced Lighting Course. Instruction was for three hour sessions on eight nights. Not surprisingly (since I was the RI Chapter's Founding President), I was asked to be the instructor. I agreed to teach the first night and help select an instructors for each of the other sessions. Eight lectures would have required a great deal of time and preparation. Also, in addition to giving me some publicity, it allowed me to help some of my contacts to get some notoriety. My lecture also gave me an opportunity to scope out some future employees.

Don't let yourself get roped into a multi-night teaching engagement at a local college. It is very time consuming with little benefit, poor pay, and (in most cases) no student appreciation.

New Service Lectures

Every time that you start a "new service," try to be a guest speaker at any professional organization whose members might use your service or recommend you. We had a local mayor who had the reputation of being available to speak at the "opening of an envelope"; my criteria was not much higher. Prepare a PowerPoint presentation and hand out your announcement. If the organization actually does a mailing, try to get the program chairmen to enclose your announcement so those who don't come to the meeting will receive your information. At the meeting, don't pass out the announcement until after your lecture because attendees may read it instead of listening to you. Take the opportunity to make new contacts.

Code – Cycle Seminar

Codes are not updated yearly; they are updated on a cycle, usually every three or four years. Consider holding a mini-seminar for your clients' tradesmen and technical staff. I recommend a 1 ½ to 2 hour seminar (instead of a 10 hours) covering the highlights. Your client will see that you are keeping up with the new changes, and it improves your relationship with the client's staff. Hold it after working hours, and break for a light dinner and soft drinks.

At one of these mini-seminars, we had about 8 attendees, and when the pizza arrived in two large boxes, my secretary set it up in the conference room. To be neat, she cut the tops off of the boxes and accidently cut the arm off of someone's jacket. She was mortified. I told the "victim" to buy a new jacket and send me the bill; he graciously declined. But I think of this memory every time that I eat pizza.

Major Seminar

When something *dramatic* happens, seize the opportunity.

In 2003, we had a tragedy in Rhode Island. 100 people perished in a fire at The Station nightclub. This catastrophic event was the impetus for a dramatic overhaul of our state fire code. The most revolutionary thing about this new code was that it was retroactive; the "grandfather clause" did not apply. All existing buildings were required to meet the new code.

I had recently been appointed to the "RI Building Code Standards Committee" and was too busy to take part in the overhaul of the fire code. But once it became law, I decided to put on a "free" seminar to educate fire officials and building owners of the new impact.

All my project managers were expert fire alarm system designers, and we had kept up with the proposed changes on a daily basis. But we spent a lot of time to make sure that we understood which building types required which upgrade and the required time table. I decided that my staff would be the "panel of presenters" and "field the questions." I personally introduced our services with a PowerPoint presentation, describing the advantages of hiring a consulting engineering firm to design fire alarm system upgrades.

I rented the largest banquet hall at the fanciest, centrally located hotel in the state for a grand buffet breakfast meeting. We did a mailing to our mailing list and to the mailing lists of all the Chambers of Commerce throughout the state. We did radio advertisements (1 minute spots liberally mentioning our company name) starting 10 days before the seminar. Note: Ethically, advertising by engineers is severely frowned upon, but these were "Public Service Announcements" sponsored by an engineering firm, so not a problem. I had many sleepless nights wondering if we would make incompetent fools out of ourselves and provide breakfast to only a handful of fire officials.

We had over 500 guests, and our seminar was an "enormous" success. It generated well over half a million dollars in fire alarm system design fees over the next 5 years and promoted other types of engineering work for us throughout New England.

I am certainly not saying to take advantage of the misfortunes of others. But I am saying to look for opportunities, have the courage to proceed, and do it *first class.*

After the seminar, I mailed a new service announcement to all attendees and made a personal phone call to all who were potential clients. I thanked them for attending and inquiring about their needs. I also asked if they knew of anyone who might also need our services. If I got a referral, I always started the conversation by saying, "I'm calling at the request of . . . ." Always ask for the job.

ENTERTAIN CLIENTS & POTENTIAL CLIENTS

Lunch

Try to associate a client (or potential client) meeting with lunch. Ask him to meet you at a restaurant for lunch, or suggest a meeting at his office followed by lunch, or arrange a meeting at his office at 11:30 a.m. and after the meeting suggest lunch. Try to pick a not-too-busy, upscale, quiet restaurant where you will not be rushed and where your conversation is unlikely to be overheard.

The purpose is to relax the client, avoid interruptions, create a chance to form a friendship, and make the client feel a little bit beholden to you. I'm not suggesting that you can "buy" the client with a lunch. But you want a little extra time to get to know him personally over lunch.

I like a great Italian restaurant on Federal Hill in Providence: "Camille's." I often held luncheon meetings there. I knew the waiters and they knew me; I was a "generous tipper." They always referred to me as Mr. Gaskell, and they would stall the meal until they got the "hi sign" from me. Later, they brought the "desert cart" instead of the desert menu. Anyone who referred a large project or important client to me could expect to have a luncheon at this fine restaurant.

Dinner

Dinner is an opportunity for the spouses to establish a friendship. Personal relationships are important because the construction industry is a "problem" business and consulting engineering is a "problem solving" business. Your client is more likely to divulge a problem to you (and to forgive you) if you (and your spouses) are friends.

Other Entertainment Opportunities

- Broadway Productions – *The Providence Performing Arts (PPAC) was a client of mine, and I had a friend who could get me front row seats.*
- Concerts – Tickets to "sold out" venues can be obtained on the internet.
- Boat Cruises – *I had a friend who owned a mini-yacht that I would charter to take clients to events on Narragansett Bay: The Tall Ships, America's Cup Trials, Newport Jazz Festival, etc.*
- Company Night – Consider inviting a few special clients to Company Night. See Chapter 15 – Human Resources.

I believe that most of my work came from superior engineering, not from the entertaining of clients. But entertainment opportunities are a way of showing your clients that you appreciate their business.

I was surprised to find that a number of "business friends" became "personal friends." Some of our life-long best friends started out as "business friends." And even though my wife passed away several years ago, these friends have not forgotten me; I still see them on a regular basis. I am truly blessed.

A Word of Caution

Federal government employees are prohibited from taking "gifts" from government contractors (you).

I don't consider buying lunch for someone a "gift," but don't be surprised if a government employee declines your invitation or insists on paying for his own lunch. Dinner at your home would be an alternative that might work for both of you.

Changing Attitudes

When I had the manuscript of this book reviewed by engineer friends, several told me that many potential clients resist forming a friendship with their consultants.

I had a few clients like that, and some hired my firm for all of their projects. Most of these were facilities directors who, I believe, were trying to avoid the appearance of undue influence regarding my continued selection.

However, I am being told that many of the selections are now being made solely based on "price." If you are in a market that seems to be unduly influenced by price, make a concerted effort to standout from your competitors. Concentrate on the methods recommended in this book, including:

- Keep up-to-date with the latest technology.
- Gain credentials to build up your resume and brochure.
- Publish magazine articles, distribute reprints, and gain a reputation as an expert.
- Be the smartest guy in the room. Prepare white papers, memorize them, and share them with your staff.
- Prepare marketing materials, and implement methods that will make your firm standout from your competitors.
- Prepare an operations manual that emphasizes quality control and service to your clients.
- Hire carefully, train, and supervise your staff and treat them well and with respect. They are your greatest asset.

SEND NOTES OF CONGRATULATIONS & THANK YOU

Congratulations Notes
Don't miss an opportunity to send a note of congratulations. As your secretary culls through the newspaper (news articles and people in the business news, etc.), FedBizOpps (FBO) database, and other sources of leads, she should be looking for opportunities for you to send a note. An award, a promotion, an appointment, and a selection for a new project are opportunities. Don't just restrict this to people that you know. Have your secretary give the typed note to you for your signature along with the news article. This gives you the opportunity to add something personal, make a phone call, or not send the note at all.

Thank You Notes
Anytime that someone does something nice for you, send a "handwritten" note. If you have lunch with a client and he pays, send a note, even though you thanked

him at the time. Even if you paid, it doesn't hurt to send him a note thanking him for meeting with you. If a client has you and your wife to dinner at their home bring some fresh flowers in a vase and possibly some good wine. Also, send a thank you note.

A NICE OFFICE

An impressive office will project an image of success and accomplishment. Most clients assume that a successful consulting engineer must be an expert in his or her specialty and will provide exceptional service. Once your firm is well-established, upgrade your office space.

After being in business for about 10 years, I bought an office building. One of my major clients donated the services of their interior design department as a house warming gift. The renovations cost me more than I expected, but I planned to be there for the rest of my career. I justified the expense on a personal basis, not just a business basis.

My staff were on the upper level, and on the lower level was a reception area, conference room, copy and fax rooms, and my personal office. My office had large mahogany double doors with etched glass vision panels, a fire place, wall-to-wall broadloom carpeting, and was furnished with antiques. I felt a little guilty for spending so much money on it, but I **smiled** *every time that I entered the room.*

When a client wanted me to reduce the fee that I had quoted, I would invite him or her to my office for coffee. After we entered my office, my secretary would come in carrying a tray with coffee, china cups, and a plate of cookies. Often, the subject of fees never came up.

This reminds me of a somewhat related story.

On a recent vacation, I stopped in Denver, CO. I saw a beautiful old red sandstone 3-story building with a rounded front. It looked out of place because it was surrounded by parking lots and the nearest building was 12 stories. My guess was that this building was on the "National Register of Historic Places," in which case, it can never be destroyed. Out of curiosity, I crossed the street and found the "Registry Plaque," proving that I was right. This building dated back to the 1870s and was previously an engineer's office; his "shingle" is still hanging in the window. It reads: University Trained Engineer . . . Problem Solver . . . Technical Consultation — ½ hr. = 25 cents . . . Ideas Developed . . . Patents Protected . . . New modern science approach . . . All projects CASH in advance . . .Thomas J. Schering – Professional Engineer.

I bet that after reading this "shingle," a potential client would look up at this classy building and fork up the two bits without hesitation.

OPEN HOUSE

When you start your practice, you probably don't want to hold an open house party because you are working out of your home or an economy space. Also, you probably can't afford the cost.

However, in 5 to 10 years, when your practice is well established and you move to grander quarters, it may be time for an open house.

Send out nice engraved invitations, and be prepared for a crowd. Remember that your work in progress is confidential; don't leave anything unpublished on display. Have plenty of food and/or appetizers. Serve coffee and soft drinks. If you serve beer or wine, have each guest be given tickets (liability issues); no hard liquor and no drinking by the staff. Be prepared that people may open doors and drawers and look through any documents that are not locked up. Make sure that the entire staff is properly dressed and make it a "first class" event.

PARTIES

By now, you must be convinced that I am a "party animal." That isn't really true, but I do believe in celebrating important occasions with a party.

Having a party every 10 years to celebrate the firm's longevity is not too frequent. If you add a new partner, have a party to introduce him to your clients. If a key employee celebrates 25 years with the company, throw the "old fart" a party.

Many people have Christmas parties, but it is a busy time of year, and they are soon forgotten. Hell, it's Friday, let's have a party.

OUTLINE SUMMARY

- **Obtain E&O insurance**: Do no not "stamp" (seal) any documents until you have professional liability insurance (Errors & Omissions). See Chapter 8 – Legal, Accounting & Insurance.

- **Seek clients & projects:** First, recontact the potential clients that you visited when preparing your Business Plan.

- **Expand your sources for leads:** Include those on your contact list, consulting engineers of a different specialty, land surveyors, building inspectors, and utility company representatives. Also, search the internet and newspapers.

- **Seek private clients:** Include contractors of your specialty, housing authorities, hospitals, colleges and universities, property managers, manufacturers, developers, banks, law firms, and federal, state, and city agencies.

- **Offer new specialty services:** There is usually no competition for specialty services and no limitation on fees. Examples (related to electrical) include: EMF investigation and mitigation, power quality studies and monitoring, UPS systems, and arc flash calculations.

- **Always consider public speaking opportunities:** This is especially important when you are trying to promote a new service or new specialty. Also, hold seminars each time that the code of your discipline is updated. This shows clients that you are keeping up-to-date and gives you the opportunity to nurture your friendship with their tradesmen.

- **Seize an ppportunity:** When something dramatic happens, be ready to take action. I am certainly not saying to take advantage of the misfortunes of others. But I am saying to look for opportunities, have the courage to proceed, and do it *first class*.

- **Entertain clients & potential clients:** If a problem occurs with the services of your firm, clients are more likely to tell you and allow you to make corrections if they know you and your spouse socially. They are also more likely to give the next project to a "friend."

- **Send notes:** Never forget to send thank you notes, and look for opportunities to send notes of congratulations. You don't even need to know someone to recognize their achievements.

- **Open houses and parties:** These are great ways to thank your clients, show off your celebrity clients, and tell all about new specialties and exciting projects.

PROJECT PHASES

INTRODUCTION

Discover how to divide your contracts and your time cards into "phases" to simplify your accounting. Find out which phases are great for your "architectural" clients and those that work best for "private" clients. Realize when your specifications should include "or approved equal," "no substitution," "base bid," or "one of the following with no substitution." Learn how alternatives and your selected bidder list will avoid aggravation for you and your clients.

A REFRESHER

I described the various **"phases"** of a typical project in Chapter 2 as follows:

> Architects hire engineers to draw system plans for their buildings, including electrical, mechanical (heating, ventilating, air conditioning, and plumbing), fire protection (sprinklers), structural, and civil. Sometimes, very narrow specialties are required, such as acoustical. The electrical systems include utilities serving the building (power, telephone, data, cable TV, and fire alarm), lighting, power distribution, fire alarm systems, telephone distribution, cable TV distribution, and any other electrical system that the particular building might require.
>
> The consulting engineer is responsible for designing within the architect's budget limitations and coordinating with utility companies and inspection authorities. At the end of the design phase, the

consultant prepares a specification document detailing the material requirements and system functions. During bidding, he attends pre-bid meetings, clarifies issues, and prepares addenda for the architect to issue to inform bidders of changes in the requirements. After a contract is awarded, the consultant reviews/approves shop drawings, detailing all equipment that his trade contractor proposes. During the construction phase, he visits the job site to record progress and clarify the contract documents. At the completion of the construction phase, he prepares a punch list detailing corrections to the work, if needed.

In this chapter, I will describe the **tasks** for each of these "phases" in more detail. In the next, Chapter 12 – Fee Proposals, I will explain how the **fees** are determined for each of these same phases.

For "**architectural**" clients, I recommend the following breakdown: (The percent indicates both the effort and the associated fee.)

MY BASIC METHOD OF ALLOCATING PHASES

- Study Phase – (separate optional phase)
- Design Phase – (75%)
- Bidding Phase – (5%)
- Shop Drawing Review Phase – (10%)
- Construction Meetings, Field Observations & Reports Phase – (10%)

I used this method of allocating phases for two reasons:

- It avoids the following argument from architects that "You were not involved with the preliminary or design development phases, so I should not have to pay you for these phases."
- It allowed me to bill for shop drawings in the first few months of construction.

Study Phase

For new buildings, a study is seldom needed. But for renovations and additions, it is more likely to be required. It is an evaluation of existing conditions to determine how the renovations and/or addition will be accommodated by existing services and systems and often includes a written report.

For example: Let's consider the "electrical" impact of a renovation and addition. Will the existing services be adequate? (Electric, fire alarm, telephone and cable.) Are existing systems expandable or will they have to be replaced or supplemented? (Fire alarm, communications systems, emergency/standby systems, etc.) Do the present codes require replacement of functioning systems? The report should also include a description of new systems proposed.

If you are unable to get paid extra for the report, suggest a verbal report to the architect and the owner's representatives. If you give a written report to the architect, make sure that he "officially" shares it with the owner's representatives. This may help you substantiate a possible future request for a redesign fee.

The architect will usually bind your report in a separate section in his report along with the reports of his other consultants. If so, ask him for a copy of his format. Otherwise, print it on your own stationary in your own format. If he wants hard copies, ask how many. "Are they to be 3-hole punched? Are they to be bound in our covers?" You probably will not need to attend his presentation meeting unless requested to do so. If you do attend, be prepared to make a presentation.

Design Phase

Includes the following tasks:

- Detailed site investigation.
- Attendance at design meetings.
- Conference memos of design meetings:
  I required my project managers to bring a list of proposed systems and electrical features to the first design meeting (See **F-17** in Chapter 13 – Operations Manuals). They document the decisions made at the meeting in a conference memo to the architect. (Don't send anything directly to the architect's client unless directed to do so by the architect. It is better to include a request that the architect forward a copy to his client.) This first meeting is where most of the important decisions are made. This memo gives the architect an early opportunity to change his mind, gives you recourse if changes are required later, and it keeps you informed—if you don't personally attend the meeting. We usually didn't bother with conference memos of subsequent design meetings unless major design decisions changed. Most design decisions were

documented in the next progress drawing submission. I developed a special conference memo form. Many of my clients told me that they had never before received a conference memo from a consultant. STANDOUT by providing "superior service" to your clients.

- Preparation of the drawings (plans):
  This phase starts when the architect sends the CAD and BIM files of the building floor plans (shells) to you. As the design progresses, more and more information keeps getting added (and changed) until the drawings are finally complete.

- Preparation of the technical specifications:
  This is a written document that details the requirements of each of the items shown on the drawings. You write this for your disciplines, and it is incorporated into the project manual by the architect.

- Approvals:
  Consulting engineers are also expected to get pre-approvals from utility companies and inspection authorities. Unfortunately, some engineers ignore or fail to document this important step. As an electrical consulting engineer, I was responsible for coordinating the electric service, telephone service, fire alarm service, and cable TV/Internet service for my projects. Before we even started the drawings, we estimated the loads (see **G-6** in Chapter 13 – Operations Manual) and sent them to the local power company (we also had a form letter) along with a site plan drawing showing the proposed location for their transformer, and we requested a meeting and/or direction. We also had a form letter that we often sent to the architect during the bidding phase requesting that he inform the owner that "extra costs" may occur during construction due to the lack of response from the power company. Most fire alarm superintendents were cooperative. We would call them initially to verify the code requirements, and they usually gave us the service requirements over the phone. At the completion of design, we met with the superintendent, reviewed the design, and made modifications, if needed, to meet his approval. Cable TV and Internet requirements could also be handled over the phone; wiring for both usually went in the same conduit. We followed through with a copy of the pertinent plans and specifications to each. (See form **G-6** Approval Verification Letter in Chapter 13 – Operations Manual.)

- Coordination Sheets:

    These are a series of forms used to coordinate major systems and equipment with the other project consultants, vendors, and the architect. I believe that I was the first consulting engineer to ever use these, and I believe that they circumvented many coordination problems on my projects. They are intended to avoid duplicating or overlooking items required by stating who is responsible for each related item. For electrical, they include generator, elevator, HVAC, plumbing, and fire alarm. Prepare similar forms for your discipline. See **E-4** Generator Coordination in Chapter 13 – Operations Manual for an example.

Bidding Phase

Contact your Selected Bidder List to inform them that this project is out to bid. Although most architects will not allow sub-bids to be restricted to your list, the more "friendly" the bidder, the better. See more about a Selected Bidder List in Chapter 9 – Marketing Materials.

Your project manager should "field all calls" on his projects. Make sure that your project manager has the latest copies of the drawings and specifications handy, and direct your staff to forward any calls to him. He is the most knowledgeable person regarding interpretations of the drawings and specifications of this project. Resist the temptation to answer questions yourself. Some questions can be answered by explaining where the information can be found on the drawings or in the specifications. Sometimes, the item was omitted or unclear on the contract documents. If so, a "tentative determination" can be given, but tell the caller that it is "not official" until an addenda is issued by the architect. Start a draft of the addenda for your trade.

On major projects, your project manager may be asked to attend a pre-bid meeting. This is a meeting to explain the *highlights* of the project to the bidders and field their questions. If the client/architect requests your personal attendance, bring your project manager to the meeting with you. He will be in a better position to answer difficult questions. Make sure that he is prepared to make a presentation (if asked to do so at the meeting) and to take notes for a possible addenda.

Prepare the addenda for your trade. Any changes, clarifications, or additions to the plans and specifications must be documented and issued to the bidders in the form of an addenda. Usually, it must be issued at least one week before bids are due. This is the architect's duty, but it is your job to provide the finished sketches and written words for your trade. Make sure that your project manager keeps abreast of your firm's due dates (usually before the issue date).

It is usually not necessary for you or your project manager to attend the bid opening. But attend, if requested.

Shop Drawing Review Phase

Once your trade contractor is selected, call and congratulate the contractor's project manager. Explain: We want to work together to produce a really nice project that we will all be proud of and one that will result in more work for both our companies. If you see an easier way to do something, call our office to review; usually, all we care about is the end result. Please carefully review the systems and product packages that your vendors propose, and compare them to the specifications; we don't want to waste a lot of time arguing over obviously inferior products. If problems arise, let's talk and resolve them. Extras will only make us both look bad. Does that sound like a plan?

After a contract is awarded, the consultant reviews/approves shop drawings detailing all equipment that the contractor proposes. The architect describes the procedure in the front end of his project manual. Usually, the trade contractor sends his shop drawings to the general contractor (GC), who forwards them to the architect, who forwards them to the respective consulting engineer. Don't accept shop drawings directly from your trade contractor. However, occasionally, an unofficial pre-review meeting is acceptable and can save time and effort. The technical section for your trade specification should list the information that you require regarding shop drawings. Stamp each copy with your shop drawing stamp and note approved, approved as noted, revise and resubmit, or rejected. Keep a copy for your files, and send the others back to the architect with a cover letter recommending action. This must be done in a timely manner or you may be accused of holding up construction. Instruct your project manager to take a "preliminary" look at all shop drawings within 24 hours; this will allow time to call in a vendor for assistance, if needed.

I include telephone "questions" and meetings with contractors and venders (except at the job site) in this phase category. Document answers given and decisions made in your job folder. Make sure that "controversial" decisions are reviewed with you. Do not delay in responding to inquiries from contractors. Without an answer, they may proceed with their "best guess," which might be bad for both the project and for you. However, listen carefully to the contractor's explanation and reasoning. He has a more intimate physical knowledge of the project, and his solution may be better than yours. Don't let your pride get in the way of the best solution. Always "thank" the contractor for calling, even if it was a dumb question. The next question may save your neck.

Clarification sketches or drawing revisions should also be included in this phase. Always consider requesting additional compensation for drawing revisions that are not a result of your mistake. Make sure that your project managers are aware not to proceed with revisions without reviewing them with you first. A timely request for additional compensation will get more attention; don't hold your breath for payment if you don't request it before doing the work or you don't submit the bill until after the architect has already sent a final bill to his client. If payment is denied, suggest doing the changes in words rather than drawing revisions. That will usually take much less time.

Engineers, architects, and owners *cringe* when they hear the word "extra." But, unfortunately, extras are a reality on many projects. Mistakes/omissions sometimes occur no matter how careful you and your staff work. "Shit happens." Resist the temptation to force the extra cost down the contractor's throat. First, try to work it out behind the scenes; sometimes, changes can be made to offset the cost and not affect the overall quality of the project. But don't trade it off on a different project for a different owner.

If the problem comes up too late in the project or if the amount of money is too great to "sweep under the rug," meet with the architect (with hat in hand) to discuss the problem. Most projects have a contingency fund for unforeseen added costs. If some of this fund is still available, you may be off the hook. If not, you and the architect are going to have to meet with the owner to contritely explain the problem and divulge how much extra funds are required. Make sure that the architect reviews with the general contractor to determine any associated extra work and the GC's "markup" on the sub-contractor's work.

Remember, the standard of care for architects and engineers is not "perfection." Even though you made an error or omission, you may not be liable for the added cost. Some professional liability insurance companies have a "pre-claims" provision that allows engineers to report the suspicion of possible future claims and receive advice from a local experienced construction claims attorney at no cost and no increased premiums. When, or if, to take this step is a matter of judgment. I used this service a couple of times for claims that never materialized. I was pleased with the advice and did not notice an effect on my premiums. See Chapter 8 – Legal, Accounting & Insurance for details.

Construction Meetings, Field Observations & Reports Phase

Usually, site visits during construction are required of consulting engineers. These are referred to as "field observations." Do not call them "supervision of construction" or "inspections"; that is not what you do, and that term implies responsibility that is beyond your function. If you accept a contract that excludes field observations, you are taking a risk. A problem discovered in the early stages of construction could avoid the same mistake from occurring hundreds of times. Also, problems are more easily and cheaply corrected while the walls and ceilings are still open. If construction phase services are canceled from your contract, carefully document your objections and concerns.

Usually, once a week, the architect and general contractor hold a construction meeting to review progress and resolve problems. Each of the sub-contractors are required to attend, but the consulting engineers are usually not unless there is a problem with their trade. Find out the day and time of these meetings, and avoid field visits at that time. If the architect sees you, he will expect you to stay for the entire meeting. In any case, your trade foreman will be tied-up in the meeting and not be free to assist you. Exclude or limit construction meetings in your contract.

Once your trade contractor is on site full-time, make your first construction observation, and bring your project manager with you. Meet privately with your trade foreman, and introduce your project manager as the go-to person in your office. Explain (as you did with the contractor's office project manager) that "We want to work together and help each other so that we all end up looking good. If you see an easier way to do something, call our office to review; usually, all we care about is the end result. Let's avoid extras; they don't help either of us. If a problem comes up, talk to my project manager and see if we can resolve it without getting your office or the general contractor involved. Does that seem like a plan?" Don't be surprised if he is not enthused because often the bonuses of construction foreman are directly proportional to the "extras" that they can find or create.

In quoting your fee, limit your duties to a specific number of field observation visits plus (usually) one punch list observation by your project manager. This limits unrealistic expectations by your client and allows room for negotiation before you start the project. In fact, if it turns out to be a problem project, it may be in your best interest to make some additional visits without compensation.

When your project manager arrives at a job site, he should first report to the general contractor's site office (usually a trailer). Sign in to the "visitors' log" (if provided), and enquire regarding the progress of your trade. Then, find your trade foreman, and review the progress in detail (including rough percentages of each item of work in each section of the project). Get the correct spelling of his name, and note how many tradesmen he has on the site today and what particular work is underway. Also, inquire about any questions or problems or ways that you can make his job easier. (Something as simple as relocating a light switch or receptacle a few inches can save him time and aggravation. If a problem arises later, he will "owe" you.) Next, make a tour of the site with the foreman, and verify the progress and compliance with the plans and specifications. If you find a discrepancy, discuss it with him; it may be unimportant and not require correction. If the discrepancy must be corrected, and the foreman agrees that it will be done, make note of it, but exclude it from your report. When you go to the site the next time, bring a copy of your notes and last report. They will remind you of what progress is new, help you remember the foreman's name, and remind you to verify the correction of the discrepancy.

I recommend a field observation form. Start your report by saying, "The following is the progress since our last report." Distinguish between what the foreman tells you and what you actually observe. If the foreman says, "The piping in the slab is complete and the pour will be on Friday," say in your report, "Most of the conduits appear to have been installed in the floor slab area. The foreman reports that the concrete pour is due Friday." If the foreman says, "The electrical inspector was here on Thursday and approved everything," state the following: "The electrical foreman reported that the electrical inspector was on-site last Thursday and did not note any code issues." Use technical terms; avoid slang. However, make sure that your report can be understood by a "laymen." Your report goes directly to your client (the architect, in most cases). He will distribute the copies. Do not send copies directly to anyone else. However, the owner/developer, project's bank, project's insurance company, etc. may eventually get copies, so these reports must be clear and limit your liability as much as possible.

At the completion of the construction phase, prepare a "punch list" detailing corrections to the work, if needed. Have your project manager bring your office record set of the drawings and specifications, and compare each system for each room to the actual construction. If you have made frequent and diligent field visits, there should not be any major discrepancies. Where possible, put general notes, like: "Many switch and receptacle plates are missing due to painting in progress." This avoids making the same comment many times. Try to keep the report as short as possible to avoid making the sub-contractor look bad. Also, try to note inaccessible areas so that you are not accused of overlooking problems in these areas.

In your contract, include that the architect is responsible to follow through to make sure that the "punch list" items are complete. But if these items are too technical for him to handle, it will probably be in your best interest to make one more site visit and report. Call the sub-contractor first to verify that the work is complete.

It is not unusual to get calls from the architect, sub-contractor, or building owner/user weeks, months, or even years later. It is bad public relations (PR) and unwise to ignore these calls. Be patient with the caller and try to offer a solution, if feasible. Instead of telling them to call the sub-contractor or vendor, offer to do it for them this time, but tell them to do it next time. If necessary, visit the site to analyze the problem along with the sub-contractor or his vendor.

For **"private"** clients, I used the following breakdown:
(The percent indicates both the effort and the portion of the associated fee.)

THE AIA METHOD OF ALLOCATING PHASES

- Study Phase – (Separate Optional Phase)
- Preliminary Design Phase – (0–15%)
- Design Development Phase – (15–30%)
- Construction Documents Phase – (30–70%)
- Bidding Phase – (70–75%)
- Construction Administration Phase – (75– 100%)

When you work for an "architectural" client, you are only responsible for a portion of the project. (In my case, electrical.) You work for the architect. He is in charge and writes the "front end" of the project manual, including the general conditions, bidding conditions, and the contract for construction.

Conversely, for "private clients," you are in charge and perform the functions of the architect. You write the "front end" of the project manual and coordinate the work of other consultants and, sometimes, the work of an architect, if needed.

I recommend the use of AIA documents. Therefore, it makes sense to break down the phases to match the AIA method.

Study Phase

The study is the same as for my basic method of allocating phases. However, the scope of projects that you handle for private clients will primarily be in your specialty. The result of the study is a written report including a description of the proposed project together with options, a cost estimate (including your fee), a time schedule (including design, bidding, and construction), and, usually, an 8 ½ x 11 sketch showing the relative locations of the major elements. Present bound copies at a meeting with your client at his office. Don't just plop the reports on the conference table and say, "here it is." Before the meeting, highlight the important parts (in your copy), and read or "paraphrase" these parts at the meeting.

Assuming that the client's reaction is favorable, ask for authorization to proceed. If they say yes, tell them, "We will get started immediately. I will get my standard contract to you within a few days." If the client requires a purchase order, say, "Please refer to my standard contract in your P.O. and attach a signed copy to it." (But, usually, they only refer to your Scope of Work and phases and don't attach your standard contract.) If the client uses his own contract form, say, "Please refer to my Scope of Work and phases in your contract." In any case, don't actually get started until you have a signed contract or purchase order.

Often, the "study phase" precedes the actual project by a year or more and is used to get a budget and scope of work for funding. It is important that the budget includes your fee so that it is not overlooked in funding. This is your opportunity to quote a generous fee because your fee is not the focus of the study.

If a regular client doesn't have funds for a study, consider a "mini-study" without compensation. This will make the client beholden to you for this and other projects. Bury the fee for the study in your generous design fee.

Preliminary Design Phase

This usually includes 15% progress prints (three copies stamped "Progress Prints"), a preliminary cost estimate, and a preliminary project schedule. Present them at a meeting with your client including typical catalog cuts of major equipment, if appropriate.

When the building owner has a Facilities Department or Maintenance Department, it is usually best to review their preferences at the preliminary design review meeting. Prepare a form for your trade similar to **H-7** in Chapter 13 – Operations Manuals.

The preliminary review meeting is usually a good time to discuss restrictions regarding specified brands. The usual choices are "or approved equal," "no substitution," "base bid," or "one of the following with no substitution."

"Or approved equal"

This means that the brand (and usually a catalog number) is the standard for appearance, function, and quality, but the contractor can submit another brand for the engineer's review/approval. Use this when it is not feasible to list three or more choices. It leaves the issue open for argument, but it is the contractor's responsibility to convince the engineer that the item being proposed is equal. Be prepared to defend a decision to reject a submission at a meeting with the architect, owner, general contractor, sub-contractor, and sub-contractor's vendor. I recommend having the specified vendor review the submission and provide a written critique. Don't reject submissions for insignificant reasons. Try to work with vendors who are reputable and reliable and only represent quality manufactures. *For example, I used "or approved equal" for lighting fixtures where there can be 50 or more types on a project.*

"No substitution"

This means to provide exactly what is specified. Avoid this wherever possible. This gives the specified vender a license to steal. Look around for at least one other brand that offers an equivalent product and service. If a product is truly unique, this restriction may be necessary, but make sure that the client/owner approves of it in advance. Instead, consider the following.

"Base bid"

Alternatively to stating "no substitution," consider requiring the "base bid" to be the specified brand, but leave a place on the bid form for an alternative brand of the contractors choosing and a bid adjustment amount. This helps to keep the specified vendor honest and gives the owner a chance to accept a reduced price. Also include requirements for vendor experience and a maintenance facility within a reasonable distance to the job site. This will avoid buying from a new and inexperienced vendor located 500 miles away. *I often used this for generator installations and fire alarm systems. It worked well when an owner had multiple installations and wanted a single maintenance contract after the included first year.*

"One of the following with no substitution"

List three or more acceptable brands and don't allow substitutions. This is the best solution, when feasible. Again, include requirements for vendor experience and a maintenance facility within a reasonable distance to the job site. *Again, I often used this for generator installations and fire alarm systems.* But avoid designing multiple system alternatives.

Design Development Phase

At this point, a final project scope and a description of systems should be developed and presented as an outline specification. Usually, include 30% progress prints (three copies stamped "Progress Prints"), a design development cost estimate, and a design development project schedule. Present them at a meeting with your client.

Construction Documents Phase

This is the phase where you prepare the drawings/plans and specification for bidding and is the bulk of your work. Usually, the preliminary drawings/plans are upgraded to become the design development drawings/plans and then upgraded again to become the construction documents.

The meetings for this phase are similar to the preliminary and design development meetings. Usually, one or two plus a final are all that are needed.

If a major element of the project includes utility services, it is advisable to include the owner's representative at meetings with the utility company. If your client is present and is aware of how undecided that they are and how often they change their minds, he will understand that it is not your fault when changes occur during construction.

Bring a copy of a "draft" of the project manual to the final review meeting. Again, before the meeting, highlight the important parts (in your copy) and read or "paraphrase" these parts at the meeting.

If feasible, include some "alternatives" in the bidding. Alternatives are things that can be added to or subtracted from the project to allow it to meet budget.

This can avoid the trouble, expense, and delay of "re-bidding." Additive alternatives are usually best; contractors are more likely to offer a discount to increase the contract price. *In my practice, I found that adding work in certain areas (floors or wings of the building) worked best. Painting of raceways, heavy duty generator enclosures, and nicer lighting fixtures were other frequent alternative options.*

Also, at the final review meeting, provide a copy of your selected bidder list, and recommend that only these bidders be invited to bid. See Chapter 9 – Marketing Materials regarding how to present this and what assurances to get from the owner. Usually, a selected bidder list will not be allowed on government projects.

If your selected bidder list is approved, there is no need to publish an invitation for bids. Notify your selected bidders, and verify their availability and willingness to bid. However, if bidding is open, include an invitation for bids in your project manual. Make sure that the owner places advertisements in the local newspaper (and/or government publications). Coordinate the dates and allow adequate time, especially during a holiday period.

Complete the approval process. See "Design Phase" previously in this chapter.

Distribute coordination sheets as referred to previously in this chapter.

Bidding Phase

Arrange for printing of an adequate number of sets of drawings and project manuals. The cost of these should be reimbursed by the client. Get a deposit from the bidders to assure that documents are returned. Electronic PDF copies on a CD are now common and are often provided at no charge to the bidders.

As previously described in this chapter, your project manager should "field all calls" regarding this project. Call any bidders who have not picked up documents after one week and encourage them to bid. If you are not sure that you will get at least three bids, consider adding bidders. At the end of the second week, call each of the bidders and ask if they have any items that should be clarified in an addenda. Issue any addenda, if required.

Have bids submitted directly to the client in a sealed envelope that is not to be opened until the bid opening date and time. For government clients, hold a "public" bid opening and tabulate the bids, including "alternatives." Distribute copies of the tabulation, congratulate the low bidder, and arrange a meeting for the contract signing. For private clients, I recommend a "private" bid opening. After the bid opening, call the low bidder to congratulate him and arrange a meeting for the contract signing.

With the permission of the client, I recommend sharing the bid tabulations with the low bidder. Tell him to review his bid and that if he made a mistake, he can withdraw the bid if he wishes, but it cannot be increased. It is better for the client to have a more expensive contract with the "second lowest bidder" than to force the low bidder to proceed with a project that he priced too low and on which he may try to cut corners.

Although you will not be signing the contract, I recommend that you attend the contact signing. Strange things can occur; if the contractor shows up with his own contract, your client might sign it if you are not there. For government projects, the client will prepare the contract. On other projects, you will have included a contract in the project manual. Complete it with appropriate dates and bring it to the contract signing. Agree on the start date ahead of time; it is not unusual for the contractor to need 2 or 3 weeks to mobilize (assemble staff and materials).

Construction Administration Phase

Most of what was covered under "Construction Meetings, Field Observations & Reports" previously in this chapter also applies here except that you are also performing the services that the architect usually handles.

The first meeting during the construction phase is called the "Pre-Construction Conference." This is the meeting where the basic construction requirements and procedures, which you included in the project manual, are reviewed. Prepare a form similar to **I-8** Pre-Construction Conference Memorandum. See Chapter 13 – Operations Manual. Prior to the conference, customize the form to match the requirements of this particular project. Read the requirements at the conference, fill in the blanks, and add any additional items reviewed. If possible, attend this initial conference with your project manager.

Schedule construction meetings on a day and time agreeable to the client, contractor, and your project manager's schedule, usually, weekly. In your project manual, you should have included an agenda for each of these meetings. On government projects, the owner's representative may chair the meeting. Otherwise, I recommend that you or your project manager conduct the meeting and later distribute meeting minutes to all in attendance. This is more work for you but gives you control of the meeting and the minutes.

Don't require your consultants, if any, to attend construction meetings unless you know of a problem with their trade. But make sure that they make the agreed-upon field visits and reports at appropriate intervals. Their field reports should go directly to you so that you can review them before you forward them to the others.

Make sure that the punch list items are completed, including those of your consultants.

At the completion of the project, there is a lot of "closeout" paperwork to complete. It is tedious but necessary. Don't overlook it or neglect to follow through.

Ten months after "final completion," call the client, ask how the project is doing, and ask if he would like to make a "warrantee review" with you and the contractor. This is an opportunity to make any corrections needed before the one year warrantee expires. It is also a good time to talk about future projects. (Don't list this as a separate phase because the client may hold back part of your fee until it is complete. It is probably better to not mention this item ahead of time.)

OUTLINE SUMMARY

Architectural Clients

- **Phasing:** For "architectural clients," phasing includes study, design, bidding, shop drawing review, construction meetings, and field observations, including reports.

- **Study:** A study phase is more likely needed for renovations or additions. It is an evaluation of existing conditions to determine how the renovations and/or addition will be accommodated and often includes a written report and cost estimate.

- **Design:** The design phase includes detailed site investigation, design meetings (including conference memos), preparation of drawings, preparation of technical specifications, and requests for approvals from utility companies and inspection authorities.

- **Bidding:** The bidding phase includes attendance at a pre-bid meeting, responding to questions from bidders, preparing addenda, and attendance at the bid opening.

- **Shop drawings:** The shop drawing review phase includes review and processing of shop drawings, responding to questions from contractors' staff, and preparation of clarification sketches or drawing revisions.

- **Construction meetings & field observations:** This phase includes attendance at job site meetings, field observations and reports, and a "punch list" final observation.

Private Clients

- **Phasing:** For "private clients," phasing includes study, preliminary, design development, construction documents, bidding, and construction administration.

- **Study:** A study phase is a written report describing the proposed project, including options, a cost estimate, a time schedule (including design, bidding, and construction), and, usually, an 8 ½ x 11 sketch showing the relative locations of the major elements.

- **Preliminary design:** The preliminary design phase usually includes 15% progress prints, a preliminary cost estimate, and a preliminary project time schedule.

- **Design development:** The design development phase usually includes 30% progress prints, a design development cost estimate, and a design development project time schedule.

- **Construction documents:** The construction documents phase is the phase where you prepare the plans and specification for bidding and is the bulk of your work. The review meetings for this phase are similar to the other phases, and the number depend upon the scope and complexity of the project. Preparation of the specifications includes both the technical specifications and the front end of the project manual. Requests for approvals from utility companies and inspection authorities are also necessary.

- **Restrictions on brands:** Review with the client what brands you plan to specify for major equipment. Also, review the specification method: "or approved equal," "no substitution," "base bid," or "one of the following with no substitution."

- **Alternatives:** Getting a price for adding or deleting certain items can avoid rebidding, if your estimate is not accurate.

- **Selected bidder list:** Avoid construction headaches by convincing your client to use your selected bidder list.

FEE PROPOSALS

INTRODUCTION

You will realize why RFPs and RFQs are so important to both you and your clients and how to appropriately respond. Learn what questions to ask when your client is seeking a fee proposal. Understand which fee methods are customary, which methods to avoid, and why an estimate of hours is essential. Comprehend how simple it is to uncover the architect's compensation and the fee that he expects to pay you. Discover never before published "Difficulty Tables" and "Fee % Curves," developed over 35 years of professional practice. Finally, see what a "winning" fee proposal agreement letter looks like.

RFPs & RFQs

RFPs are "Requests for Proposals" and RFQs are "Request for Qualifications." In both cases, these are notices of the need for architects and/or engineers. Both types are advertised in newspapers, or in the FedBizOpps (FBO) database, or elsewhere. Both require a submission of qualifications. But an RFP usually also requires a submission of a fee proposal or an hourly rate schedule.

You may become aware of these by calls from previous clients, potential new clients, or from engineers of a different specialty.

RFPs/RFQs – AS A CONSULTANT

On most projects, you will not be the "prime professional," you will be a "sub-consultant," usually to an architect. For example: If a hospital is building a new wing, they will hire an architect to handle the whole project. He would be the "prime professional" and you would be a "sub-consultant" to the architect in your specialty.

On the other hand, if the hospital wants to add a generator, they might hire an electrical engineer to be the "prime professional," who might, in turn, hire an architect as a "sub-consultant" to design a generator building and a mechanical engineer as a "sub-consultant" to design the exhaust, ventilation, and fuel supply requirements.

Assuming that you are not qualified to be the "prime professional," notify all existing clients who would likely be qualified and interested by e-mail or fax. Encourage them to respond, include a list of your previous similar projects, and request to be part of their team.

Attend the "pre-bid" conference. Be seen and get a copy of the attendance list. E-mail or fax qualifications and a request to be part of the team of the architects that were not accompanied by an engineer of your discipline. Follow through with a phone call explaining why you are the best qualified consultant for the project.

RFPs/RFQs – AS PRIME PROFESSIONAL

Pay special attention to projects for which you are qualified to be the "prime professional." On these, you will sit in the driver's seat and not have to give a portion of your fee to an architect. Many of these will lead to repeat work and, often, to referrals.

Read the request carefully and respond completely, in the order listed, with the number of copies requested. Also, include other appropriate marketing materials. Use your version of form **F-20** "RFP/RFQ Response Letter" (see Chapter 13 – Operations Manual), as an example.

PREVIOUS CLIENTS

If the request is from a client who works exclusively with your firm, handle the request yourself. Alternatively, assign the proposal to one of your project managers whom the client likes. Make an appointment to meet with the client. If it is a renovation or addition, try to meet at the site. Otherwise, meet at the client's office. If it is a major project, bring one of your project managers with you to hear the details first hand.

In any case, bring your version of Form **F-16** "Fee Proposals" (see Chapter 13 – Operations Manual). These are questions to assist in determining scope and fee requirements.

POTENTIAL NEW CLIENTS

Handle these the same as "previous clients," except try to go personally.

REFERRALS

Call referrals and try to speak with a firm "principal" to make an appointment. Do not identify the person who gave you the lead, unless previously authorized. If they ask, I say, "I heard through the grape vine; salesmen can't keep a secret." Before the call, make a list of reasons why your firm is the best suited for this particular project.

PROJECT SCOPE

Take careful written notes. If the client doesn't mention the following in his explanation of the project, ask:

- Is this a single-use building or multi-use?
- What is the area (sq. ft.) of each use?
- What is the area (sq. ft.) of "new," "renovation," and "addition"?
- What is the project budget?
- What is the project schedule?
- When will we be able to get started?
- What is the schedule for each phase: study, preliminary, design development, construction documents, bidding, and construction administration?
- How long is construction expected to last?

Try to get a copy of preliminary "floor plans," if available.

After returning from the meeting, prepare a preliminary scope (see page 3 of form **F-16** "Fee Proposals" in Chapter 13 – Operations Manual). Obviously, you will need to revise this form to suit your discipline/specialty.

FEE AGREEMENT METHODS

Often, the client dictates the method of payment. The following are the most common options:

Fixed-Fee

This is a specific dollar amount for each phase of the project. I found this to be the most common. Assuming that you carefully define the scope and detail assumptions and exceptions, it avoids arguments and gives the client a specific fee amount. Occasionally, there is a dispute about the percent complete of each phase for monthly billing. But, assuming the project doesn't get canceled, that problem eventually gets worked out.

Percent of Construction Cost

Your fee is a percent of the "low bid" for the construction of your discipline/specialty. Some of my clients used this method. It is important to state that the construction cost includes all "designed alternatives." For example, let's assume that a decision is made to get an "additive alternative price" for an emergency/standby generator and emergency distribution system in lieu of battery units. The electrical engineer should get a design fee based on a percent of the cost of both designed options.

Hourly – (not-to-exceed)

Avoid this whenever possible; it always causes arguments. The not-to-exceed number is never more than what a fair fixed-fee would be. Therefore, there is no "upside" for you. If you are honest, you will soon go out of business.

Others

Others are "per diem," "multiple of payroll cost," "hourly without limit," etc. State DOT (Department of Transportation) projects are often done on a multiple of the payroll method. But, periodically, they audit your books and often disallow expenses (like rent for your office space in a building owned by your company or that you own personally). When this happens, get out your check book. Consider methods of payment carefully before accepting assignments. Never accept a project on a "handshake" or a promise that "we will work it out later."

ESTIMATE HOURS

Regardless of your fee payment method, ALWAYS estimate the hours of work that the project is expected to require.

At this point, resist the temptation to jump to the next section and base your fee on a percent of your discipline's construction cost. If you don't have a rough idea of what the project is going to cost you in man hours, you may end up "winning" a LOSER. Also, this process will uncover what "exceptions and assumptions" that you should include in your proposal. See form **F-15** "ESTIMATE OF HOURS" in Chapter 13 – Operations Manual. Again, you will need to modify this form to suit your discipline/specialty and staff.

In estimating hours, include the project manager who met with the client, or (if you went alone) include the project manager that you plan to assign to the project. This allows you to get their input and often uncovers facts about the project that they forgot to tell you. Also, it gets them to "buy-in" to the budget of hours. But avoid letting them "inflate" the hours budgeted.

I used the following "staff" categories:

- PM – Project Manager (A person who can handle most of the specialty with minimal supervision.)
- CT – CAD Technician (In some cases, the project manager "redlined" prints for a CAD drafter. Other project managers did the CAD drafting themselves. If so, put these hours under project manager.)
- DD – Division Director
- ADD – Assistant Division Director
- SA – Senior Associate (The daily supervisor for the PMs.)

Use the (blank) preliminary floor plans as a visual guide, and take your best "crystal ball" guess regarding the hours. Make sure that your form includes all the things that your firm does (and sometimes does) to complete the services that you provide.

After completing the hourly estimate form, thank the project manager for his time and proceed with the formal proposal privately.

VERIFY CONSTRUCTION COST

You will need up-to-date ESTIMATING BOOK(S) or CDs that include:

- General New Construction Cost ($/sq. ft.).
- Costs for your trades (percent of total or $/sq. ft.).
- A geographical multiplier.

RSMeans Company www.rsmeans.com is one company that produces estimating books and CDs that are updated annually.

ESTIMATE THE ARCHITECT'S FEE & YOUR ASSOCIATED FEE

The first step is to estimate the "difficulty" of this type of project for the architect. This is not an exact science, but I have prepared Figure **12-1** "DIFFICULTY LIST" to assist you.

The second step is to estimate the "general" construction cost of each of the areas of the project. Use the latest version of one of the many good "Construction Cost Estimating Books." (Unless you can find a "combined book," you will need two or more books: one for general construction and others for your trades.) They each have two related tables: one is the average sq. ft. cost and the other is an adjustment factor for your geographical area. Be sure to use both.

The next step is to enter the difficulty and the construction cost on the correct FEE PERCENTAGE GRAPH.

See Figure **12-2** "FEE % GRAPH FOR NEW CONSTRUCTION."

See Figure **12-3** "FEE % GRAPH FOR RENOVATIONS."

DIFFICULTY LIST (1 OF 2)

BUILDING TYPE	A	B	C	D	E
COMMERCIAL					
Auto Dealership			X		
Cinema			X		
Mall/Plaza (shell only)			X		
Restaurant			X	X	
Retail Store			X		
Retail Store (Shell only)		X			
Supermarket			X		
RESIDENTIAL					
Apartments		X	X		
Condos/Townhouses		X	X		
Single- Family Homes (multiple)		X	X		
Single-Family Homes (Custom)				X	
Assisted Living			X		
EDUCATIONAL					
Administrative Offices			X		
Athletic Complexes		X	X		
Audutoriums/Performing Arts			X	X	
Classrooms			X		
Dormitories		X	X		
Elementary School			X		
Junior/Middle School			X		
High School			X	X	
Laboratory/Research				X	X
Library				X	X
Special Needs				X	
Multi-Purpose			X		
HOTEL/MOTEL					
Convention/Conference Center		X			
Hotel			X		
Motel/Inn		X			
INDUSTRIAL					
Manufacturing (Custom)			X	X	
Manufacturing (shell only)		X			
Researh and Development				X	
Warehouse with Office		X			
MEDICAL					
Hospital				X	X
Medical Office Complex			X		
Nursing Home			X		

FIGURE 12-1

DIFFICULTY LIST (2 OF 2)

PUBLIC FACILITIES	A	B	C	D	E
Aquariums				X	
Auditoriums				X	
Art Galaries			X	X	
City Halls			X	X	
Civic Center			X		
Correctional Facilities			X	X	
Court Houses				X	
Fire/Police Stations			X	X	
Government Buildings			X		
Marinas			X		
Museums				X	X
Neighborhood Centers		X			
Parking Garages		X			
OFFICES					
Banks			X		
Office Buildings (Tenant Fit-out)			X		
Office Buildings (shell only)		X			
RECREATIONAL					
Arena			X	X	
Health Club		X			
Recreational Center		X			
Skating Rink			X		
RELIGIOUS					
Church			X		
Multi-Purpose		X			

NOTE:
Where the table has 2 listings, choose
the one that more suits your project or
Interpolate between the two choices.

FIGURE 12-1

FEE % GRAPH FOR NEW CONSTRUCTION

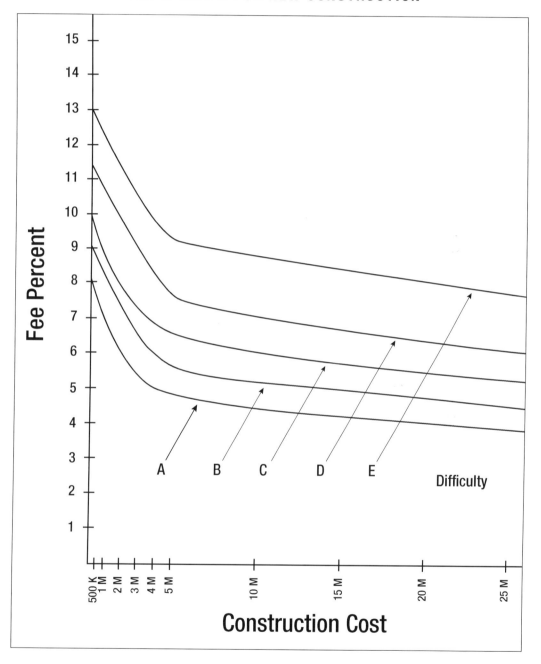

FIGURE 12-2

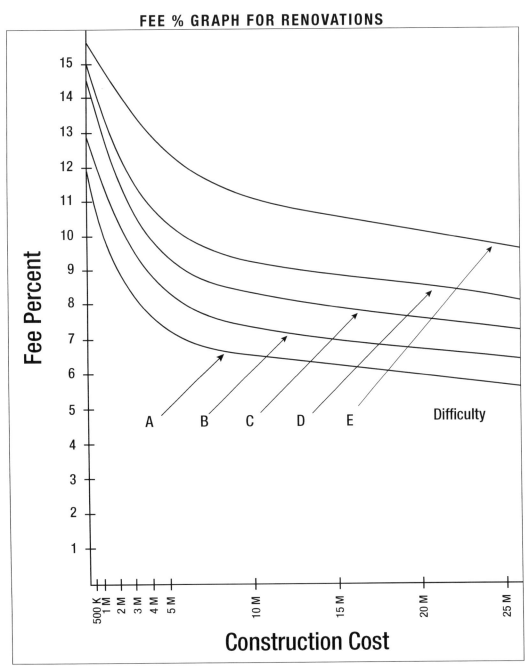

FEE % GRAPH FOR RENOVATIONS

FIGURE 12-3

Example

This may sound a little complicated, but an example will reveal how simple (but not exact) it really is.

Assume that the project is an existing high school located in the state of Rhode Island. The new project is to renovate a portion of the existing school and add a new library.

- Existing building size: 40,000 sq. ft.
- Portion to be renovated: 10,000 sq. ft.
- Library addition: 15,000 sq. ft.

First, convert the above areas to "general" construction cost.

- High school: $197/sq. ft. x 1.22 x 10,000 sq. ft. = $2,403,400
  (Note: I used the factor 1.22 to adjust the costs for the Rhode Island area. You would, of course, adjust for the area of your project.)
- Library: $215/sq. f.t x 1.22 x 15,000 sq. f.t. = $3,934,500
  (Note: I have ignored the 30,000 sq. ft. of existing high school that is not being renovated. As a consultant, you will have to spend some time assessing existing systems and possibly designing replacements or modifications if these systems are not expandable to meet the needs of the new project. But the architect will probably not get more fee since his work in these areas is minimal. However, include your extra time in your budget of hours.)

Second, use Figure **12-1** to determine the "difficulties."

- High school = "C"
- Library = "D"

Next, use Figure **12-2** to determine the architect's fee for the library addition because this is new construction.

- Library addition – 7.5%

Use Figure **12-3** to determine the architect's fee for the renovation.

- High school renovation – 9.8%

Then, determine the budgets for mechanical and electrical construction.

- Library addition
  - Mechanical: 15% x $3,934,500 = $590,175
  - Electrical: 9% x $3,934,500 = $354,105
- High school renovation
  - Mechanical: 18.1% x $2,403,400 = $435,015
  - Electrical: 12.9% x $2,403,400 = $310,038

The architect (or other prime professional) expects you to work for a "**portion**" of his fee. When I first started in practice, it was ⅔ and later increased to ¾. You need to check with other consultants in your area of practice to determine what the architect is expecting. I have used ¾ in this example.

Finally, the mechanical and electrical engineering fees are determined.

- Mechanical:
  Library addition: 7.5% x ¾ x $590,175 $33,197
  HS renovation: 9.8% x ¾ x $435,015 $31,973
        Total mechanical fee $65,170
- Electrical:
  Library addition: 7.5% x ¾ x $354,105 $19,918
  HS renovation: 9.8% x ¾ x $310,038 $22,787
        Total electrical fee $42,705

These are the "approximate" fees that the architect should be expecting from his mechanical and electrical consultants. Compare these to your "estimate of hours." If they differ substantially, recheck both.

Things to consider are:

- What other work do you expect to have during the likely schedule of this project? (Deadlines usually creep.)
- How much competition do you think that you have?
- How good a client is this?

- Is this phase 1 of a multi-phase project?
- The question usually boils down to "How hungry are you?"
- If you are a "startup" and the partners are doing most of the work, you can put in some extra uncompensated hours and cut the fee a little.
- Most firms are concerned about paying hourly employees "overtime." I never was. 5–10 hours of overtime per week makes most employees happy. But any more than that makes them less productive. However, I believe that limited overtime actually improves your bottom line. Your employee's hourly billing rate should be 2.5 to 3 times what you actually pay him in order to cover benefits, taxes, overhead, and profit. If you pay an employee $60/hour, his billing rate is about $175. That rate covers all the items listed based on a 40 hour work week. If he works overtime, you pay him $60 x 1.5 = $90, plus a little extra in payroll taxes, electricity, and heat. But the cost to you, for that extra hour, is a lot less than $175.
- Some projects are "losers." Try to pass up most of them.

I have just shared with you the fee "secrets" that took me 35 years to perfect. Apply my advice and use your best judgment; your proposals will win you work.

FEE PROPOSAL LETTER

Prepare a fee proposal letter using Figure **12-4** as a guide. Don't put your fee proposal letter in your operations manual. This is not something that you want to share.

This document needs to be revised to suit your practice and disciplines. I am not qualified to offer legal advice. Make sure that your legal counsel reviews and approves your final document. Most of the items in my fee proposal letter are self-explanatory, but note the following:

The SCOPE OF PROJECT is unique for each assignment. Delete the example and insert the scope for your project.

The SCOPE OF ELECTRICAL and ASSUMPTIONS & EXCEPTIONS get heavily edited for each project.

For architects, I recommend dividing the FEE into four parts:

Drawings and Specifications	75%
Bidding	5%
Shop Drawing Review	10%
Site Observations/Meetings/Reports	10%

See Chapter 16 – Project Phases for details. Even if your estimate of hours does not match these percentages, list the dollars for each phase in these percentages of the total, unless the client insists on a different allocation.

I recommend printing the Contract Terms and Conditions on the back of the signature page. I usually included all of them. If a client called and objected to any of them, I would *reluctantly* say, "Since you are such an important client, cross that item off on both copies." I am not sure that any of these items would hold up in court; I never reviewed them with my legal counsel. But I got very few objections to them.

FEE PROPOSAL LETTER (1 OF 5)

FEE PROPOSAL
(On your letter head)
Figure 12-4

(Client address)

Attn.:_____

Regarding: (Insert name and location of project)

Dear:_____

The following is our proposal for **Electrical Engineering Services** on the subject project:

SCOPE OF PROJECT: (Insert brief description) Example:

The project is to renovate a portion of an existing High School and to add a new Library.

   Existing Building size: 40,000 sq. ft.

   Portion to be renovated: 10,000 sq. ft.

   Library Addition: 15,000 sq. ft.

SCOPE OF ELECTRICAL :(Include only those that apply and add new, if needed)

- Services (electric, telephone, fire alarm, and cable)
- Power Distribution (panels, feeders and branch circuits)
- Interior Lighting
- Exterior Lighting (perimeter, walkways, driveways, landscape, façade, parking)
- Emergency Battery Lighting
- Emergency/Standby Generator and associated equipment and distribution
- Exit Signs (led type with emergency back-up)
- Telephone/Data distribution system (raceway and/or cable)
- Telephone/Data system equipment
- Security Alarm Systems
- Lightning Protection System
- Cable TV Raceway and/or Cable Distribution System
- Fire Alarm System (addressable with master box)
- Fire Detection System
- Carbon-Monoxide detection system
- Nurse Call System
- Intercom System

FIGURE 12-4

FEE PROPOSAL LETTER (2 OF 5)

ASSUMPTIONS & EXCEPTIONS: :(Include only those that apply and add new, if needed)

- All existing electrical systems will be removed. There is no need for us to draw a demolition plan. However, we will visit the site to observe existing conditions.
- Design review meetings will be held in Rhode Island.
- If construction is phased over a number of years, bidding and construction phase fees would obviously increase.
- This project will be designed as a single project with a single bid phase and a single construction phase with one electrical contractor.
- We will verify the adequacy of the existing services (power, telephone, fire alarm, cable TV…etc.). However, the fee quoted assumes that they can remain in place and are adequate in size.
- We have assumed that adequate sources of (power, telephone, data, fire alarm, cable TV…etc.) are available in the immediate vicinity of the project and will be identified for us.
- Our work does not include upgrades of other areas of the facility.
- AutoCAD base drawings will be furnished to us.
- Construction phase services (review of shop drawings, meetings / site observations, etc.) are not part of this proposal. However, we will be available at our standard hourly billing rates.
- Written electrical load data is to be provided to us on all equipment.
- Cuts of equipment and a complete schedule of electrical requirements will be provided to us.
- Electrical load data (connected and demand) for the building will be available to us.
- Only one electrical service is required to the building.
- Removal of existing utilities is not part of our work.
- A dimensioned electrical stub-up plan for equipment is not required.
- Lighting will be laid out and selected by you.
- You will provide layout of lighting, receptacles and communications outlets.
- Your Lighting Consultant will produce a separate set of drawings and specifications for interior and exterior lighting and controls.
- Existing fire alarm system is expandable for the needs of this project.
- Our presence is not required at committee meetings, variance hearings, pre-bid meeting or pre-construction meeting.
- The fee assumes that an electrical transformer vault (or modification to an existing vault) will not be required.
- Computer room has no special requirements such as power conditioning or a UPS system.
- An existing building evaluation study and report is not required.
- Detailed cost estimating is not required.
- A detailed outline specification is not required.
- Fieldwork to be scheduled in advance at mutually agreed times. A knowledgeable person will be assigned to accompany us while at the facility and to provide access to all necessary areas.
- You will assist us in estimating proposed and future loads.

FIGURE 12-4

FEE PROPOSAL LETTER (3 OF 5)

- Review and coordination with the local electric utility company, telephone company, superintendent of fire alarms, building officials and agencies is not part of our work.
- We have included __ site visit/observations/meetings during construction plus a punch list, (Total of __ visits). Add $_____ for each additional visit.
- We have assumed that the following is not part of our work: design of pole bases and testing of soil conditions.
- Meetings to review our report are not included. Add $____ each.
- Re-design services are not included.
- Specifications will go on the drawings.
- We will provide "technical" specifications. Our work does not include "front end" (General Conditions, Bid Forms, etc.).
- We have not included the cost of outside consultants: (Architect, Structural Engineer, Geotechnical Engineer, etc.).
- The enclosed "disclaimer" will be attached to the report and is hereby made a part of this agreement. It is understood that this is a study and not a design. Drawings and specifications are not included.
- This proposal does not include involvement with alternative or renewable energy sources such as co-generation, fuel cells, wind or solar.
- We cannot enter confined spaces (manholes, etc.) and cannot enter spaces containing wiring or equipment over 600 volts (vaults, etc.). Also, we cannot examine exposed live parts. If information regarding the above is needed, an electrician may be required. The cost of an electrician is not included in this proposal.
- LEED design and accreditation services are not included.

FEE:

We propose the following fee:

Drawings and specifications...$

Bidding Phase ....$

Shop Drawing Review, Questions, etc................................$

Site Observations/Meetings during construction and

Including written reports...$

TOTAL ....$

Reimbursable: Printing, postage, travel, parking, lodging, and equipment rental will be billed at cost. Mileage will be billed at $0.___/mile.

FIGURE 12-4

FEE PROPOSAL LETTER (4 OF 5)

Our usual conditions are attached, which you should read carefully. If our proposal is satisfactory to you, please sign and return it to our office.

Sincerely,

(Your company name here)

Your Name Here, Credentials

Your Position Here

Accepted by:_____

Printed Name/Title:_____

Date:_____

☐ Check here if purchase order is required.

FIGURE 12-4

FEE PROPOSAL LETTER (5 OF 5)

<u>CONTRACT TERMS AND CONDITIONS</u>

1) Late charges are assessed at 1.5% per month from date of invoice or 18% per year. All collection costs, including attorney's fees and any court fees are to be paid by client. 2) If the invoice is not paid in thirty (30) days the consultant may terminate the contract without waiving any claim or right against the client and without any liability whatsoever to the consultant. 3) Obligations of the client to pay the consultant are not contingent on client obtaining any approvals, acceptances, permits or reimbursements from any parties, individuals, organizations or agencies. 4) All charges are computed portal to portal from (Insert City and State). 5) If consultant is ordered to stop work after agreement to this proposal, he will be paid his standard hourly billing rates, up to the limit of the quoted fee. 6) All consultants' documents: original drawings, estimates, specifications, field notes, reports and data are the sole and exclusive property of the consultant as instruments of service. All consultants' documents are copyrighted. All rights reserved. 7) The client (and subsidiaries of the client) agree not to attempt to hire (or discuss employment with) any employees (or former employees) of (Insert Company Name) until one year has passed, since their employment by (Insert Company Name). 8) Any controversy or claim out of or relating to this contract, or the breach thereof, shall be settled by arbitration in accordance with (Insert your State). Arbitration Association Rules and Judgment upon the award rendered by the arbitrator(s) may be entered in any court having jurisdiction thereof. The client understands and agrees that (Insert Company Name) may file a mechanic's lien upon the land/improvements in the event of nonpayment by client. 9) Estimates of Construction Cost, if any, represent our best judgment as design professionals familiar with the construction industry. However, it is recognized, that neither the Engineer nor the Owner has control over the cost of labor, materials or equipment; over the Contractor's methods of determining bid prices; or over competitive bidding, market or negotiating conditions. Accordingly, we cannot and do not warrant or represent that bids or negotiated prices will not vary from the estimate.

FIGURE 12-4

OUTLINE SUMMARY

- **RFPs & RFQs:** Be on the "look out" for RFPs and RFQs and respond ASAP.

- **Sub-consultant:** For requests where you will be the "sub-consultant," notify your appropriate clients who may want to be the "prime consultant." Express an interest in being on their team along with the documentation showing why your firm is the best choice.

- **Prime professional:** When you are qualified to be the "prime professional," respond with document **F-20** RFP-RFQ Response Letter and listed attachments.

- **Fee proposal scope:** When clients ask for a fee proposal, bring form **F-16** to the meeting. It will assist you in gathering the necessary information.

- **Fee methods:** Most fees are a fixed amount or a percent of construction; avoid other methods.

- **Estimate hours:** For <u>every</u> project, estimate hours, regardless of the method of fee payment. Develop your own form similar to form **F-15** Estimate of Hours.

- **Architect's fee:** Estimate the architect's fee based on the "Difficulty Tables" and "% Curves" that were developed over 35 years of professional practice.

- **Your fee:** Estimate your fee based on a portion of the architect's fee and the calculated construction costs of your trades.

- **Fee proposal:** Finally, prepare your "winning" fee proposal letter with the help of Figure **12-4.**

CHAPTER 13

OPERATIONS MANUAL

INTRODUCTION

Understand how your Operations Manual is the "guidebook" to your engineering practice and will be a major ingredient in your firm's success. Learn how to organize yours, and see samples of information and forms for each category.

GENERAL

As I advised in Chapter 2, start keeping a notebook of information as soon as you start working. Also, index your code book and highlight significant sections. The information that you use constantly (like wire capacity and conduit fill tables for electrical engineers), copy and enclose in a sheet protector to keep handy. In addition, accumulated copies of things that you might use again: calculations, forms, letters, technical articles, utility company requirements, white papers, and other reference information.

After I established my own engineering practice and began hiring employees, I wanted to standardize procedures for two reasons. Most importantly, this was so that my staff would provide the same standard of service that my clients had come to expect from me. Also, I realized that by sharing information we would become more efficient and, thus, more profitable. I organized this information and put it in a 3-ring binder that I called my Office Manual.

WHAT IS AN OPERATIONS MANUAL?

Although I didn't know it at the time, I had produced what is generically called an Operations Manual.

Your Operations Manual is the "guidebook" to your engineering practice. It will be unique to your practice and, if thoughtfully prepared and well organized, will be a major ingredient in your firm's success.

The following is the table of contents that I used:

OPERATIONS MANUAL

Table of Contents

Section	Title
A	Office Forms & Procedures
B	Technical Procedures
C	Codes & Technical Issues
D	Approval Letters
E	Coordination Sheets
F	Forms & Form Letters
G	Calculations
H	Questionnaires
I	Private Clients
J	Office Policy

Office Forms & Procedures

This section was most helpful to train new employees to the basics of our operation. Included here are fundamentals, like weekly duties, time cards, and expected attitude.

Technical Procedures

This section is intended to organize the technical step-by-step approach to managing an assignment. Many seasoned project managers who joined our firm discovered steps that they had been skipping. Don't assume that those with experience are doing things the way that you expect.

I hired a project manager with almost twenty years of experience. After six months, I assigned him to a manufacturing addition project for a company that provided terminals for lotteries. This was a "fast track" project with weekly progress meetings.

My client called me after the first meeting and told me that the president of this high profile company attended these weekly meetings and that I should be there as the head of my firm. So, in preparation for the next meeting, I met with my project manager for about 15 minutes to get up-to-date, and then I accompanied him to the meeting.

When it was his turn to present the progress of the electrical, he unrolled the progress prints and said, "Here it is." No explanation, no summary, nothing. I was stunned. But I was glad that this was not the first time that I had seen the progress. I stepped in and gave a brief overview of the progress with my project manager knowledgably answering questions. After that meeting, I updated my Technical Procedures to include a paragraph on progress presentations.

Codes & Technical Issues

Most code requirements are clear, but some are subject to interpretation, and it is important that a firm be consistent. Also, some rules are specific to certain types of projects and require extensive research. Time can be saved on future similar projects by carefully documenting the investigation and including it in this section.

When you prepare a "white paper," put it in this section so that your staff can benefit from this information. I also made copies of new items and distributed them at our periodic office meetings and suggested that everyone take them home and study them so they could be knowledgeable on the topic. I encouraged them to keep a copy in their notepad; always have something worthwhile to read while waiting for anything.

Approval Letters

As stated in Chapter 11 – Project Phases, consulting engineers are expected to get "pre-approvals" from utility companies and inspection authorities. Unfortunately, some engineers ignore or fail to document this important step. After preliminary contact follow through with a copy of the final plans and specifications to document your coordination. The associated forms and form letters (relating to your disciplines) should be kept in this section.

Coordination Sheets

Coordination sheets are a series of forms used to coordinate major systems and equipment with the other project consultants, vendors, and the architect. These forms are intended to avoid duplicating or overlooking requirements by stating who is responsible for related items. This is a doubled edged sward; it affixes the blame if the drawings and specifications of the various disciplines conflict. For electrical items to be coordinated, include generator, elevator, HVAC, plumbing, and fire alarm. Prepare similar forms for your specialties.

Forms & Form Letters

All consulting engineers use many of the same forms and letters over and over again. Save time, be consistent, and don't reinvent the wheel each time. Prepare forms and form letters for your disciplines.

Calculations

As with form letters, all consulting engineers use many of the same calculations over and over again. Prepare calculation forms for your disciplines. Include code references where appropriate.

Questionnaires

These are organized lists of questions to ask at meetings/conversations with utility companies and clients. Not all questions need apply to all projects, but these questionnaires save time and avoid overlooking important questions.

Private Clients

As previously discussed, when you work for private clients, you assume the role of the "prime professional" and are responsible for many additional tasks. The forms and other materials that will assist you with this increased responsibility are filed in this section. Partially fill out these forms with information that is standard for your projects.

Office Policy

Items in this section explain to your staff the general policies of your office. Examples include not specifying any one vendor too often to avoid the appearance of collusion, definition of the standard of care that is expected of engineers, and ethical issues.

Examples

The following are one or more examples of things to be included in each category of a proposed OPERATIONS MANUAL.

A-2	Time Card
A-2 (I)	Time Card Instructions
B-1	Technical Procedures Checklist
C-19	Duct Detectors
D-10	Approval Verification Letter
E-4	Generator Coordination
F-16	Fee Proposal Scope
F-17	Systems List
F-20	RFP/RFQ Response Letter
F-21	Electrical Specifications Checklist
G-6	Load Tabulation
H-7	Specified Brands
I-8	Pre-Construction Conference Memorandum
J-1	Specifying Lighting Fixtures

TIME CARD (1 OF 2)

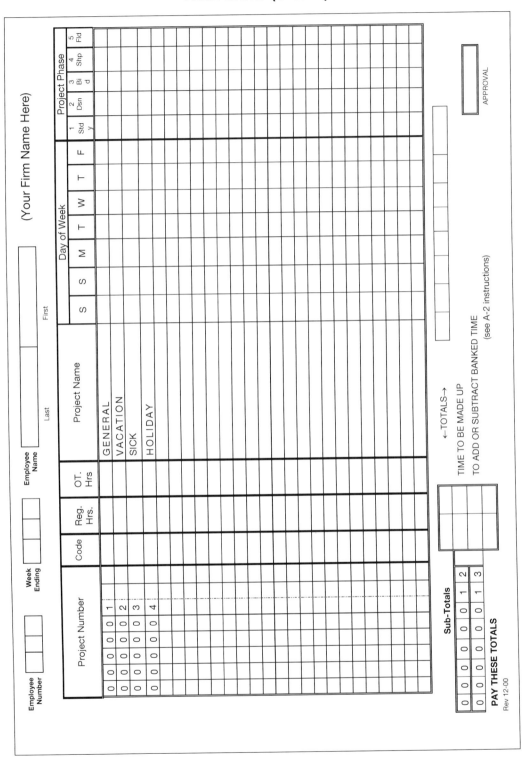

A-2

TIME CARD (2 OF 2)

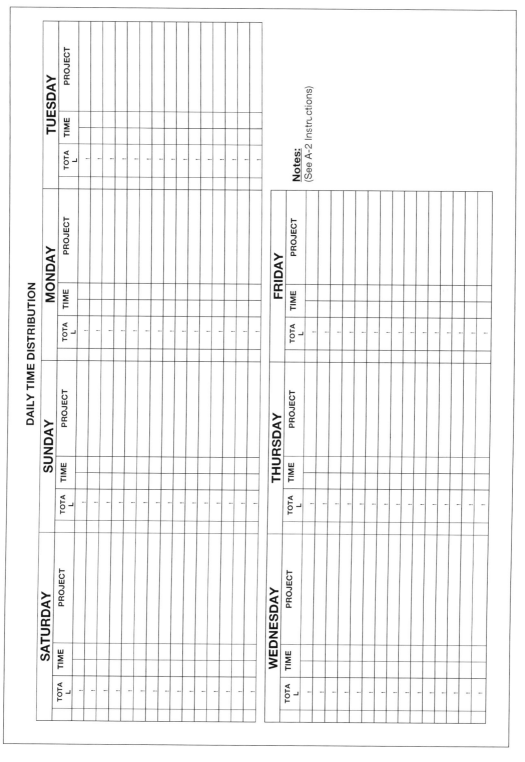

A-2

TIME CARD INSTRUCTIONS (1 OF 3)

Time Card Instructions

1. Time card form A-2 is in our operations manual. Make a copy. Carefully fill in your employee number (ask office manager) and print your name. Make about 20 copies. This way you won't have to fill in your name and number each week.

2. The week starts on Saturday and ends on Friday. Fill in Friday's date under "week ending".

3. During the week, keep track of your time on the back of the sheet, at the end of the week, summarize it on the front.

4. Under TIME, there are 2 columns. On the left indicate the time of day that you start a task and on the right, when you finish.

5. Under PROJECT, abbreviate the name of the project.

6. Under the TOTAL column indicate the total time for the interval (For example: If you have 9 – 11:30 under time, the total is 2 ½. Put the 2 to the left of the date and the ½ to the right 2 ½). You can do this daily or at the end of the week.

7. We keep track of our time in ½ hr. segments. Don't use smaller segments. If you spend 10 minutes on something, don't list it. But, the next time you spend 10 minutes on the same project, list it as a ½ hr.

8. Except when working on weekends, all employees must take a ½ hour lunch break to refresh their selves. List LUNCH under the PROJECT column and fill in the time. But do not list ½ hour under total.

9. At the end of the week, add up the TOTAL column for each day. Before 10:00 am, each Monday morning, fill in the front of the time card and give it to the bookkeeper.

10. Under "Project Name" list the projects that you worked on. Also, list the "Project Numbers" (see job list) PLEASE PRINT. If you worked on more than one phase (study, design, bid, shop, and field) of the same job, list the job twice.

11. Next, on the back of the sheet add up the time you spent on each project, each day and list it on the front (Use ½ not 0.5). As you do this, check it off in the first column on the back of the sheet. This way you won't miss any or include it twice.

12. On the front of the sheet, (at the bottom) indicate the total hours for each day. Verify that they are the same as the totals on the back of the sheet. Then add across and indicate the total hours on the front (bottom right).

13. Add the time spent on each project and list under "regular hours" or "overtime hours."

A-2 (I)

TIME CARD INSTRUCTIONS (2 OF 3)

14. "If you work more than 40 hrs. in any week, unless you are on salary, the excess hours are listed in the overtime column. See A-8 for instructions on overtime.

15. In the CODE column, indicate the phase of the project that you worked on (Study = 1; Design = 2; bid = 3; Shop = 4; Field = 5.) Note: Field work during design is still Code 2.

16. Fill in the "Sub totals" and verify that they are the same as total in item 12.

17. If the sub-total is less than 40 hours, indicate enough hours under 12 (time to be mad up) to total 40.

18. If the sub – total is more than 40 hours and you wish to "bank" some time, list it under 13.

19. Under PAY THESE TOTALS indicate the number of hours you expect to get paid in both columns.

20. "Project Managers" fill out the % complete Columns. See A-9.

21. Give completed time cards to the bookkeeper before 10:00 am on Monday. If you will be out on Monday morning, try to complete your time card on Friday or Saturday.

22. Please try to remember to fill in your time card each time that you change tasks. Also, please make sure your time card is complete before you leave each day.

23. Accurate time records are essential. We don't want to charge our clients for more time than was actually spent.

    If you arrive at 8:10, go to the rest room, tell a joke or two and actually sit at your work station and start at 8:30; your time card should say 8:30.

    All we have to sell is time. The success of the company depends upon using each minute wisely and effectively.

24. NON-PROJECT TIME

    Some time is spent that is not billable to a project. Use one of the following job numbers.

TIME CARD INSTRUCTIONS (3 OF 3)

GENERAL OFFICE 000000.01 (0.01)

The category on our time cards for "GENERAL OFFICE" is for time that is not attributable to a specific project. However, this doesn't mean that we assign every minute not spent on a project to this category.

For example, charge the following to the project that you are working on: getting coffee; going to the bathroom/ putting things away; brief unrelated interruptions or phone calls. As a general rule, you should be spending 50 minutes of each hour on a project, in order to charge a full hour to the project.

If you keep your time card up-to-date each time you change tasks, that time is included in the time of that project. Filling out the front of the time card is general office. Office meeting, office maintenance, ordering and picking up supplies are all general office. Most deliveries should be charged to the job or jobs involved. Most code research is chargeable to a specific project.

If Project Managers or CAD Technicians have more than 3 hours of general office in any week, it should be explained on the back of the time card under "notes."

FEE PROPOSALS 000005.01 (5.01)

When you assist with preparation of a proposal for a new project (site visit, estimate of hrs. or cost estimate), list your hrs. under 5.01 "PROPOSAL."

However, if your time exceeds 8 hours on any one proposal, discuss with the CEO.

TIME SPENT CORRECTING PROBLEMS OR REDESIGN

On some projects, we are paid on an hourly basis. If we have to spend extra time correcting a problem that we caused, we don't want to charge our client for it. This can happen during design or construction. For example, if we overlook an item and have to make a special field visit to work it out with the contractor. Another example would be if we had to redesign the electrical distribution system because we initially made a bad choice of voltages. Review these cases with the CEO so that we can decide the best way to handle them.

A-2 (I)

TECHNICAL PROCEDURES CHECKLIST

TECHNICAL PROCEDURES CHECK LIST

DESIGN

Section B

☐   1.   SCOPE REVIEW

☐   2.   START JOB FOLDER OR BINDER

☐   3.   FIRST MEETING WITH CLIENT

☐   4.   CONFERENCE MEMO

☐   5.   CODE RESEARCH

☐   6.   FIELD SURVEYS OF EXISTING FACILITIES

☐   7.   OUTLINE SPECIFICATIONS

☐   8.   PRELIMINARY LOAD ESTIMATE & UTILITY CONTACT

☐   9.   PRELIMINARY SITE LAYOUT
           Services (electric, fa, tel, cable), transformer location, generator location.

☐   10.   PRELIMINARY FLOOR PLAN LAYOUT & FIXTURE SELECTION

☐   11.   PROGRESS REVIEW MEETINGS (Including preparation)

☐   12.   VENDOR CONTACT & SPECIFICATION INFORMATION

☐   13.   COMPLETE PLANS

☐   14.   CALCULATIONS

☐   15.   COST ESTIMATES

☐   16.   SPECIFICATION COORDINATION

☐   17.   REVIEW OF DRAWINGS

☐   18.   COORDINATION & APPROVALS

B-1

DUCT DETECTORS

Duct Detectors:

There are two agencies with requirements for HVAC shut downs. The State of Rhode Island Fire Safety Code and the National Fire Protection Association, Article 90A.

The State of Rhode Island fire safety code does not require duct smoke detectors to shut down heating, ventilating on air condition units. Chapter 23-28.25-5 (J) requires that any system units with 2000 CFM or greater, be inter connected with the buildings HVAC controls so that fans with 2000 CFM or greater will be shut down when the fire alarm system is activated.

National Fire Protection Association, NFPA 90A Re: Air condition and ventilating systems. Chapter 4 "Controls" states the following in paragraph 4-4

1. Smoke detectors must be installed in the supply duct to automatically stop the fan for systems over 2000 CFM.

2. If a unit serves more than one story and the capacity is over 15,000 CFM, a smoke detector must also be installed in the common return at each story prior to any recirculation on fresh air inlet. The return smoke detector can be deleted if the area that the unit serves is protected entirely by smoke detectors.

There is a dilemma in the state of Rhode Island. Some municipalities do not want the duct detectors. Some say "ok put them in, but don't connect them to the fire alarm systems." Yet others like the city of Providence want the duct detectors connected to the fire alarm system but only to send a trouble signal when activated.

Therefore, we must review this item with each authority on a job by job basis.

C-19

APPROVAL VERIFICATION LETTER

Approval Verification Letter

(Your Letterhead)

(Modify to suite each situation)

_____   Date _____
_____
_____
_____

Attention: _____
                  _____

Regarding: _____
                  _____

Dear Sir:

- Thank you for meeting with me to review the electrical drawings and specifications for the subject project.

- Thank you for reviewing the electrical drawings and specifications, which we forwarded to you.

- Thank you for reviewing the enclosed electrical drawings and specifications.

It is my understanding that they are acceptable to you and that no additional items are required.

It is my understanding that they are acceptable to you with the following modifications, which we will include:

Please verify your acceptance by signing this letter and returning it to us.

Thank you for your assistance in this matter. If you have any questions or require further information, please do not hesitate to contact this office.

Very truly yours,

(Your Company Name Here)

_____

CC: _____
    Architect

                            Accepted by: _____
                                   Date: _____

D-10

GENERATOR COORDINATION (1 OF 2)

PROJECT: _____   DATE: _____

Generator Coordination

From:
  (Your Company) PROJECT MANAGER: _____

To:
  ARCHITECT: _____   PROJ. MGR. _____
  FIRE ALARM MFG. _____   REP. _____
  PLUMBING ENGINEER: _____   PROJ. MGR. _____
  H.V.A.C. ENGINEER: _____   PROJ. MGR. _____

1. GENERAL: Information based on _____ Model # _____
    Size: _____ kW, Voltage _____ volts _____ phase _____ wire
    Enclosure: YES _____   NO _____ Size _____ L _____ W _____ H
    Fuel: Diesel: _____   Propane: _____   Nat. Gas: _____   Dual : _____
    Remote annunciator: YES _____   NO _____

2. EMERGENCY LOADS: (Those that apply are checked)

    ☐ Emergency Lights & Exit Lights _____

    ☐ Heating _____

    ☐ Ventilation _____

    ☐ Refrigeration _____

    ☐ Pumps (Sump, Ejector, etc.) _____

    ☐ Elevator (s) _____

    ☐ Fire Pump _____

    ☐ Other (see Remarks) _____

3. ARCHITECT TO CALL FOR THE FOLLOWING:

    Concrete Pad _____ L _____ W _____ H, to support _____ lbs.

4. PLUMBING ENGINEER TO CALL FOR THE FOLLOWING:
    (Those that apply are checked)

    A. ☐   Fuel Tank (We suggest 72 hrs. minimum capacity)

    B. ☐   Fuel Piping

    C. ☐   Fuel Piping not required. Generator will be provided with a base tank of _____ gal.,
           for _____ hrs. of operation at full load.

E-4

GENERATOR COORDINATION (2 OF 2)

5. PLUMBING ENGINEER TO CALL FOR THE FOLLOWING:
   (Those that apply are checked)

   A. ☐ Fuel Tank (We suggest 72 hrs. minimum capacity)

   B. ☐ Fuel Piping

   C. ☐ Fuel Piping not required. Generator will be provided with a base tank of _____ gal.,
   for _____ hrs. of operation at full load.

   D. ☐ Exhaust piping

   E. ☐ Muffler installation. (muffler is furnished by Engine Mfg.)

   F. ☐ Muffler will be factory piped and mounted on enclosure. (Extend to roof if required).

   G. ☐ Piping for city water cooling _____ GPM.

   H. ☐ Piping and foot valve for day tank and pump. (Day tank, pump, lift check valve, and
   fire-o-matic valve to be factory mounted by Engine Mfg.) Plumber to furnish and
   install foot valve.

   I. ☐ Install solenoid valve (furnished by Engine Mfg.) to prevent siphoning. (If fuel tank is
   higher than engine.)

   J. ☐ Other (see remarks)

6. REMARKS:

   _____
   _____
   _____
   _____

7. ENCLOSURES:

   _____ Generator cut sheet   _____ Gas piping chart

   _____ W.P. Enclosure cut sheet   _____ Exhaust piping chart

E-4

FEE PROPOSAL SCOPE (1 OF 3)

(Your Letterhead Here)

Fee Proposals Scope

Often when we are asked for a fee proposal, I ask a Project Manager to attend a meeting or go to the site to determine scope.

Please proceed as follows:

1.   Scope

    A.   See Page 3, as a guide in preparing a written scope.

        a.   Under SCOPE OF PROJECT describe the project briefly. For example:

            New ± 30,000 s f. Elementary School

            ± 10,500 sf. addition to an office building.

            Lab renovations per attached RFP dated January 1, 20__.

        b.   In most cases, use the SCOPE OF ELECTRICAL as a guide in asking questions. Add and delete as necessary. Use pencil and be neat enough so we can hand it to the typist without re-doing.

    B.   Also review Systems List (Form F-17). But, only ask about relevant systems)

    C.   For projects with a special scope, write it out ready for the typist.

2.   Questions (ask only if appropriate)

    A.   How do you want fee broken down?

        a.   Our usual is:

            Drawings and specifications ....$
            Shop Drawing Review, Questions, etc. ....$
            Site Observations/Meetings during construction,
            Including Reports ....$_____
                          TOTAL......................................$

    B.   When do you need the fee?

F-16

FEE PROPOSAL SCOPE (2 OF 3)

C. Do you need anything else?

Company Brochure	P.E. Registration
333 Form	Firm Registration
Letters of Reference	Letter of Authorization
Firm Profile (short version)	Qualification Statement
Firm Profile (long version)	Evaluation Statement
Resumes of Key Personal	Hourly Rate Schedule
Related Projects List	

Number of copies of above _____?

D. Are electrical demolition plans required?

E. Will AutoCAD base drawings be provided to us?

F. Who will select and layout lighting?

Us?   You?   Or a Lighting Consultant?

If lighting consultant, will he have his own drawings and specs or will we incorporate his work on our drawings? All interior and exterior lighting?

G. Will our attendance be required at pre-bid meetings?
Pre-construction meetings?

H. Book spec or drawing spec?

3. Who do we address proposal to?

If new client, get business card. We need full name and title of person, address, telephone number, fax number and e-mail address.

Do we fax or e-mail?

4. Proposal

A. Prepare scope as soon as possible after meeting and notify CEO that you are ready to review.

B. Bug the CEO daily or every other day until it gets done.

F-16

FEE PROPOSAL SCOPE (3 OF 3)

SCOPE OF PROJECT:

SCOPE OF ELECTRICAL:

Services (electric, telephone, fire alarm, and cable)

Power Distribution (panels, feeders and branch circuits)

Interior Lighting

Exterior Lighting (perimeter, walkways, driveways, landscape, façade, parking)

Emergency Battery Lighting

Emergency/Standby Generator and associated Equipment and Distribution

Exit Signs (LED type with emergency back-up)

Telephone/Data Raceway and/or Cable Distribution System

Fire Alarm System (Addressable with Master Box)

Fire Detection System

Carbon-Monoxide detection System

F-16

SYSTEMS LIST (1 OF 2)

(Your Letterhead Here)

Systems List

- ☐ CLOCK AND PROGRAM SYSTEM

- ☐ CLOCKS OR CLOCK OUTLETS

- ☐ SOUND REINFORCEMENT SYSTEM

- ☐ INTERCOM SYSTEM OR CLASSROOM INTERCOM

- ☐ DOOR INTERCOM SYSTEM (Release, postal key, mailboxes, directory)

- ☐ PRIVATE TELEPHONE SYSTEM

- ☐ MEDIA RETRIEVAL SYSTEM

- ☐ DOOR CHIMES

- ☐ LABORATORY SYSTEMS (odd voltages, language lab)

- ☐ BURGLAR ALARM OR VANDAL ALARM

- ☐ DOOR ALARM (local or remote)

- ☐ CARD ACCESS SYSTEMS

- ☐ DOOR RELEASES

- ☐ TV (master antenna, closed circuit, cable)

- ☐ VIDEO SURVEILLANCE SYSTEM

- ☐ EMERGENCY BATTERY LIGHTING

- ☐ EMERGENCY GENERATORS (transfer switches, enclosures, fuel)

- ☐ EMERGENCY RELAYS

F-17

SYSTEMS LIST (2 OF 2)

- ☐ DIMMING SYSTEMS

- ☐ SCOREBOARD WIRING (or empty conduit)

- ☐ EMERGENCY CALL (elderly housing)

- ☐ SWIMMING POOL ALARM SYSTEM, GROUNDING

- ☐ FIRE ALARM SYSTEM (code minimum?)

- ☐ FIRE DETECTION SYSTEMS (smokes in housing)

- ☐ CO_2 DETECTION SYSTEMS

- ☐ NURSE CALL SYSTEM

- ☐ LIGHTNING PROTECTION

- ☐ BUILDING STRUCTURAL GROUNDING

- ☐ SNOW MELTING (Roof, Walks, Driveways)

- ☐ COMPUTER ROOMS

- ☐ UPS SYSTEMS

- ☐ HARMONIC PROVISIONS (k-rated transformers, panels, double neutrals, isolated ground)

- ☐ POWER MONITORS

- ☐ TVSS OR SURGE PROTECTOR

- ☐ THEATRICAL LIGHTING

F-17

RFP/RFQ RESPONSE LETTER (1 OF 2)

RFP/RFQ Response Letter

(Your company letterhead)

(Name & Address)

Attention:

Dear:

We wish to be considered for the project advertised in the COMMERCE BUSINESS DAILY, Dated _____ Entitled "_____."

Enclosed please find the following:

      Standard Form 330
      Our Firm's Brochure
      Standard Form 330 for our Consultant
      Brochure for our Consultant

If the scope of our work includes testing or dismantling for inspection of high voltage equipment, we propose engaging the services of (insert name of testing company). We have recently worked with them and have found them to be reliable and competent. However, if the on-site investigation requires a visual inspection only, we would provide complete in-house services.

We feel that our firm is ideally suited for this particular assignment. We are ELECTRICAL engineers. We are not just the "electrical department" of a firm that specializes in many different kinds of services. Almost every project that we handle includes power distribution and electrical systems for buildings.

Electrical systems for hospitals has become one of our specialties. The following is an outline of the recent work we have done for hospitals:

(Insert list of hospital projects including your contact person at each and a phone number.)

F-20

207

RFP/RFQ RESPONSE LETTER (2 OF 2)

Example:

ST. JOSEPH HOSPITAL-FATIMA UNIT (_____, Chief Engineer) (Tel. #)
North Providence, RI
Emergency Power - Phase 1
1000KW Generator Installation with provisions for future 1000 KW generator.
Critical Care Addition
New ICU/CCU and Telemetry Addition
Radiology Service
Radiology Suite - with 4,160 volt service, transformer and distribution.

I have enclosed a copy of our company brochure, which gives background on me and my firm. I am sure that any of our clients listed would be happy to recommend our work.

I am personally involved with all the projects of this office and will provide executive management for this particular assignment.

I believe that we have an exemplary and proven team of experienced and able personnel to perform the required services on time, within budget, and with professional distinction. We are immediately available to commence work on this project.

Very truly yours,

(Insert your co. information here)

F-20

ELECTRICAL SPECIFICATIONS CHECKLIST (1 OF 5)

ELECTRICAL SPECIFICATIONS CHECK LIST

PROJECT NAME: _____

CITY: _____ STATE: _____

YOUR PROJECT MANAGER _____ DATE: _____

CLIENT
ADDRESS: _____

_____

_____

Attention: _____

FORMAT (Get copy)   ☐ attached   ☐ will get

PROJECT TYPE: _____ New   _____ Addition   _____ Renovation

COORDINATION SHEETS

- ☐ HVAC
- ☐ Plumbing
- ☐ Generator
- ☐ Fire Alarm
- ☐ Elevator

RELATED WORK SPECIFIED UNDER OTHER SECTIONS:

- ☐ Temporary Wiring for building construction – see DIVISION 1 or ☐ DIVISION 16
- ☐ Cutting and patching – see DIVISION 1
- ☐ Allowances – see DIVISION 1
- ☐ Alternatives – see DIVISION 1
- ☐ Excavation and backfilling – see DIVISION 2
- ☐ Concrete – see DIVISION 3
- ☐ Manholes and handholds – see DIVISION 3

F-21

ELECTRICAL SPECIFICATIONS CHECKLIST (2 OF 5)

☐ Magnetic door release – see DIVISION 8

☐ Access panels – see DIVISION 8.   Or   ☐ Furnished under DIVISION 16.

☐ Painting of all backboards (on all sides and edges before mounting); painting of panels (trims and doors – 2 coats before mounting); painting of exposed electrical raceways, boxes and fittings – see DIVISION 9.

☐ Elevators – see DIVISION 14.

☐ Sprinkler flow switches and gate valve switches – see DIVISION 15.

☐ Furnishing of manual and magnetic starters for HVAC equipment – see DIVISION 15. (Edit, per HVAC Coordination Sheet)

☐ Temperature controls, temperature control wiring, interlock wiring and boiler control wiring (except as indicated on the electrical drawings) – see DIVISION 15. (Edit, per HVAC Coordination Sheet)

☐ OWNER FURNISHED ITEMS (usually furnished by Electrical Contractor) (List)
    ☐ BACK CHARGES   ☐ Available   ☐ Allowance $_____

☐ SPECIAL BRANDS
    ☐ APPROVALS BY US   ☐ BY _____

☐ BACKBOARDS

☐ REMOVALS   ☐ Relocations   ☐ PCB`s

☐ ACCESS PANELS
    ☐ Furnished by EC and installed by mason/drywall contractor
    ☐ Furnished and installed by mason/drywall contractor

☐ SERVICE   ☐ New   ☐ Existing to remain
    VOLTAGE: ☐ 120/208   ☐ 277/480   ☐ 120/240
    ☐ U.G.   ☐ O.H.   ☐ Pad Mtd. ☐ pole mounted

    Power Co: _____
    address: _____
            _____
    Contact: _____
    Tel.#   (_____)_____

☐ LIGHTNING PROTECTOR

F-21

ELECTRICAL SPECIFICATIONS CHECKLIST (3 OF 5)

☐ TVSS ☐ Main (voltage _____) ☐ Panels (voltage _____)

☐ DISCONNECTS ☐ Heavy Duty 30-60 ☐ Bolted Pressure 800+
☐ Double Throw (Manual Transfer Switch)
☐ General Duty (Economy)

☐ SWITCHBOARDS ☐ CBs ☐ Fused Switches
☐ Power Logic Metering

☐ DISTRIBUTION PANELS ☐ CBs ☐ Fused Switches
☐ Power Logic Metering

☐ PANELS ☐ Bolt-on ☐ Plug-on

☐ METER CENTERS
☐ Power Company Meters
☐ Blank covers with by-pass for future meters.
☐ Private check meters

☐ POWER MONITORS

☐ TRANSFORMERS ☐ 480 volts Delta to 120/208 volt wye
☐ Other_____

☐ NEW SERVICE GROUND ☐ Existing Service Ground to Remain

☐ WIRING ☐ CU only ☐ AL or CU
☐ In/under floor slab ☐ Underground
☐ EMT ☐ RGS ☐ Surface Metal Raceway
☐ MC ☐ AC ☐ NM
☐ Health Care ACTHH
☐ Emergency Feeders
☐ Fire Pump Wiring

F-21

ELECTRICAL SPECIFICATIONS CHECKLIST (4 OF 5)

DEVICES (Switches & Receptacles)

☐ Standard ☐ "Decora"

Color _____

Plate: ☐ Plastic ☐ SS ☐ Brass ☐ Nylon

☐ FLOOR OUTLETS (If so, spec. on drawings)

☐ TELEPHONE / DATA PROVISIONS

☐ Full ☐ Partial

☐ Backboards ☐ Ground

Tel Co: _____
address: _____
_____
Contact: _____
Tel.# ( ) _____

☐ RACEWAY SYSTEM (Exact name per drawings)

_____ ☐ Full ☐ Partial
Full Partial
_____ ☐ ☐
_____ ☐ Full ☐ Partial
_____ ☐ Full ☐ Partial

☐ EMERGENCY BATTERY UNITS (Spec. on drawings)
☐ FIRE ALARM SYSTEM ADDITION & MODIFICATION

Existing Brand: _____

☐ Control Panel modifications

☐ FIRE ALARM SYSTEM
Specified Brand: _____
Equal Brands: EST, FCI, Gamewell, Simplex, Notifier

☐ Spec. Attached ☐ Due: _____

☐ STRUCTURAL GROUNDING SYSTEM

F-21

ELECTRICAL SPECIFICATIONS CHECKLIST (5 OF 5)

☐   LIGHTNING PROTECTION SYSTEM

     ☐   Below 75 feet   ☐   75 feet or more

☐   SYSTEM EXTENSIONS & MODIFICATIONS

(Names exactly as on drawings)

	Full	Partial	Attached
_____	☐	☐	☐
_____	☐	☐	☐
_____	☐	☐	☐
_____	☐	☐	☐
_____	☐	☐	☐
_____	☐	☐	☐

☐   NEW SYSTEMS

(Names exactly as on drawings)

	Full	Partial	Attached
_____	☐	☐	☐
_____	☐	☐	☐
_____	☐	☐	☐
_____	☐	☐	☐
_____	☐	☐	☐
_____	☐	☐	☐

☐   COMMENTS: _____

_____

_____

_____

_____

_____

F-21

LOAD TABULATION

(Your Company Letterhead)

PROJECT: _____   DATE: _____
POWER CO.: _____   ATTN: _____

LOAD TABULATION

PRESENT DEMAND _____ kVA
LOAD BEING DELETED _____ kVA
NET EXISTING DEMAND REMAINING _____ X 1.25 _____ kVA

NEW LOADS:

LIGHTING:.. _____ kVA
ELECTRIC HEAT: .... _____ kVA
AIR CONDITIONING: .... _____ kVA
VENTILATION: .... _____ kVA
POWER (Receptacles, etc.): .... _____ kVA
MOTORS: (_____H.P.) .... _____ kVA
COOKING/REFRIGERATION .... _____ kVA
FIRE PUMP: (_____H.P.)................................. _____ kVA
ELEVATORS: (_____@_____H.P. .... _____ kVA
ELECTRIC HOT WATER: .... _____ kVA
CLOTHES WASHERS: .... _____ kVA
CLOTHES DRYERS:... _____ kVA
OTHER: .... _____ kVA
OTHER: .... _____ kVA
OTHER: .... _____ kVA
_____ kVA
TOTAL CONNECTED LOAD .... _____ kVA

SERVICE VOLTAGE: _____ VOLTS, _____ PHASE _____ WIRE
CONNECTED LOAD IN AMPERES: _____ AMPS
MAIN OVER-CURRENT PROTECTION: _____ AMPS
LARGEST MOTOR:
        HORSEPOWER: _____ LOCKED ROTOR CURRENT _____
        METHOD OF STARTING: _____
DATE OF CONSTRUCTION START: _____
DATE FINAL SERVICE IS REQUIRED: _____
SPECIAL EQUIPMENT: (Welders, etc.) _____

REMARKS:

☐ PRELIMINARY   ☐ FINAL

G-6

G-6

SPECIFIED BRANDS (1 OF 2)

Specified Brands

PROJECT: _____   DATE: _____

When a building owner has a Facilities Department or Maintenance Department, it is usually best to review their preferences on brands.

Our master specification currently lists the following brands/types:

SWITCHGEAR

    Square D, Cutler-Hammer, General Electric, Siemens, or National Switchboard

TVSS (Transient Voltage Surge Suppressor)

    Leviton or approved equal

POWER MONITORS (Prevents single phase damage to large motors)

    Time-Mark or approved equal

WIRE

    #8 and smaller – copper only
    #6 and larger – copper or aluminum with compression connectors
    G.E.C – copper only

SWITCHES & RECEPTACLES

    General Electric, Bryant, Hubbell, Leviton, P&S or Cooper

LAMPS

    Phillips, Osram Sylvania, General Electric or approved equal

BALLASTS

    Advance, Osram Sylvania, General Electric, Universal, Motorola, Lutron or approved equal

H-7

SPECIFIED BRANDS (2 OF 2)

FIRE ALARM

EST (Edwards), Gamewell, Simplex, FCI, Notifier or Siemens.

GENERATORS

Caterpillar, Cummins/Onan, Kohler, Generac, Superior

AUTOMATIC TRANSFER SWITCHES

Asco, Russelectric or approved equal

Asco, Russelectric only (at critical facilities)

OTHER

Approved By: _____

Printed Name: _____

H-7

PRE-CONSTRUCTION CONFERENCE MEMORANDUM (1 OF 2)

(Your Letterhead Here)

Pre-Construction Conference Memorandum

PROJECT:	**PAGE 1 OF:**
OUR JOB #:	**CONFERENCE DATE:**
LOCATION:	**PREPARED BY:**
ATTENDEES:	**COPIES TO:**

The following is a record of the major items discussed at the pre-construction conference:

1. Bid Price - The Contractor has carefully reviewed his bid and the work of the project and is comfortable with his bid.

2. Drawings & Specifications - The Contractor has carefully reviewed the drawing and specifications and does not anticipate any EXTRA work.

3. Relationship and Coordination of Contractors - This contract only recognizes one contractor, who is responsible for the work of his subcontractors. The contractor is responsible for coordinating and scheduling all work.

4. Designation of responsible personnel -

    Contractor's On-Site Foreman –

    Contractor's Project Manager –

5. List of Major Subcontractors - To be submitted.

6. Construction Schedule - To be submitted. Schedule by building and by item of work. Coordinate with "Schedule of Values."

7. Processing of field decisions and Change Orders - Engineer will document "no-cost" field changes in field reports. Changes involving cost / time-increases / decreases to be done via Proposal Request and Change Order Forms. Do not proceed with Change Orders until you receive a copy signed by the Owner.

8. Adequacy of distribution of Contract Documents - The contractor was given ____ extra copies of plans and specifications. He will notify us if he needs more.

9. Submittal of Shop Drawings - Contractor to submit 1 copy for Engineer, 1 copy for Owner, 3 copies for Owner's Manual, plus number of copies needed for contractor, his subs and his suppliers. (Total of ___) Submit direct to Engineer who will keep one copy, send one copy to owner and return remaining copies to contractor.

10. Record Documents - per Section 01010, Pages 3 and 4.

11. Use of Premises

    Trash – Remove your own trash, see 01500.

    Sanitation Facilities – Use of owner's designated toilet facilities will be permitted.

    Storage – Provide storage trailer, if needed.

    Field Office – Provide office trailer, if needed   Parking -

I-8

PRE-CONSTRUCTION CONFERENCE MEMORANDUM (2 OF 2)

12. Equipment priorities - Contractor stated that most materials and equipment are "off the shelf." However, submit shop drawings early and order equipment to avoid last minute substitutions or delays.

13. Safety and first-aid - Contractor has established procedures and will make sure that all job site personnel have adequate training. Contractor to report any injuries to Engineer within 24 hours of incident.

14. Security Procedures

15. Housekeeping Procedures - Do not leave anything (materials, equipment, trash, etc.) where they may create a hazard to anyone.

16. Project Close-out - See section 01700.

17. Project Start Date -

18. Working Hours –

19. Core Drilling – To be done after 9 a.m. Properly dispose of water and core material off site. Do not pour down owners drains.

20. R.F.I.'s – Where feasible, contact Engineer's Project Manager via telephone or during site visits for questions/clarifications. This will limit the need for "Requests for Information".

21. Deliveries – Owner's personnel will not receive or sign for deliveries.

22. Permit – Contractor to forward copy of permit to owner.

23. Review of Drawings – Contract drawings were reviewed. No exceptions were noted.

24. Requisition of Payments – Except for the 1st requisition for payment, the Electrical Contractor must submit a release of liens for all of their sub-contractors with each request for payment, this includes their supply houses where they buy materials.

25. Other

    Notice to tenants:

    Critical work sequence:

    Shut-downs:

    Holidays:

26. Next Project Meeting

    Date:

    Time:

    Place:

_____

(Your Company Name)

I-8

SPECIFYING LIGHTING FIXTURES (1 OF 2)

Specifying Lighting Fixtures

The biggest hassle that we seem to have at "shop drawing" time is lighting fixtures. We need to be fair but we need to keep the Owner's interests foremost in mind. On small projects, it is usually not worth the effort in coming up with 3 catalog numbers for major fixtures. Also, the fixture representatives are not as tenacious on re-submittals. Therefore, we accept "equal" fixtures. However, it is important to list the major features that we want, under "remarks" for each fixture.

Occasionally, on large projects, it has been our policy to list three manufacturer's names and catalog numbers in the two or three large quantity fixtures and insist that one of these three be used. However, if this does not provide three truly independent choices for the Contractors, we cannot enforce this provision because we will appear to be in collusion with the manufacturers' representatives.

To avoid problems, follow these procedures:

1. Don't always specify products represented by the same one or two agencies. Spread the work around to reps who call on us regularly.

2. To save time, it is helpful to have the rep fill out the fixture schedule for us and make a set of cuts for us. But, do not let him select his competitors. You need to carefully select these yourself. Try to make sure that you do not select apples to compare with oranges or Volkswagens to compare with Cadillac's. Make copies of the cuts on these and review them with Ed of Jack.

3. Unfortunately, calling in two competitors for catalog numbers doesn't usually work well. They often want to push something of lesser quality and usually want to be listed for every fixture, which becomes awkward and time consuming.

4. Make sure the competitors are "active" and will bid competitively and are not represented by the same agency. Don't spec agencies that are too "friendly" with the specified agency.

5. No one agency should be specified on more than ~~40 to 50% of each Project Managers work~~ *25% of each Project Managers work* (based on value). The "appearance" of impropriety is almost as bad as impropriety itself. There are no secrets in a small state like RI. If an employee here was found to have taken a "kick-back", we would probably be forced out of business. Fortunately, I am confident that this is not a potential problem.

6. Do not allow the rep to specify "special catalog numbers." This confuses the competitor and the Contractor can't get proper competitive bids. If a fixture has a special accessory that is not clearly indicated in their catalog, call for it in words.

J-1

SPECIFYING LIGHTING FIXTURES (2 OF 2)

7. To be sure that the Owner gets the appropriate rebate for each fixture, indicate the "Energy Rebate Category" in the remarks column, next to each fixture (or add a column for this).

8. Try to avoid specifying fixtures represented by unknown agencies. We may not be able to rely on them for help, if there is a field problem.

9. Our Client and the Owner expect us to be fair and reasonable. We obviously can't accept crap, because we owe the Contractor a favor. On the other hand, we can't be unreasonably protective of the manufacturer's rep who helped us during design. No two fixtures are identical. We need to be reasonable, without giving away the farm. You need to ask yourself: "Would I be comfortable, defending my position at a meeting with the Owner, architect and Contractors?"

10. The Owner benefits when the construction process moves along smoothly. We would like to avoid pissing the Contractors off by making the approval process too difficult. We may need some favors during construction. However, bear in mind that the Contractor has probably bought "per plans and specs" and may not benefit financially from our quick approval. But, he certainly won't be pleased, if he has to process the shop drawings numerous times.

J-1

OUTLINE SUMMARY

- **Operations manual:** Your Operations Manual is the "guidebook" to your engineering practice and will be a major ingredient in your firm's success.

- **Office forms & procedures:** When training new employees to the basics of your operation, have them review the office forms and procedures.

- **Technical procedures:** Organize the technical step-by-step approach to managing each assignment under technical procedures.

- **Codes & technical issues:** Most code requirements are clear, but some are subject to interpretation, and it is important that a firm be consistent. Carefully documenting code research and including it in this section will save time on future projects.

- **Approval letters:** Review your projects with utility companies and inspection authorities, and carefully document this process.

- **Coordination sheets:** Create a series of forms to coordinate major systems and equipment with the other project consultants, vendors, and the architect.

- **Forms & form letters:** Customize forms and form letters for your disciplines to make your firm more consistent and efficient.

- **Calculations:** Document your calculations with forms tailored for your practice.

- **Questionnaires:** Make organized lists of questions to ask at meetings or during conversations with utility companies and clients.

- **Private clients:** The forms and other materials that will assist you in this increased responsibility as the "prime professional" are kept in this section. Partially fill out these forms with information that is standard for your projects.

- **Office policy:** Explain to your staff the general policies of your office in this section.

DRAWINGS, SPECIFICATIONS & PROJECT MANUALS

INTRODUCTION

You will discover how logical sheet organization will please the contractors and get more of them to bid. Learn how standard details save time and increase profits. See how to easily add addenda and change orders to your record drawings and project manual and, thus, avoid costly oversights. Find out how developing a "specifications questions list" will make specification writing easier and avoid errors. Ascertain how to create "three" specification versions to serve all of your needs. Observe how to acquire a "front end specification" for your project manual and how to easily customize it for each project.

GENERAL

The requirements for construction projects are set forth in three documents. This concept is clearly defined in Document A201™ General Conditions of the Contract for Construction by The American Institute of Architects, as quoted here:

> § 1.1.5 **The Drawings**
> The drawings are the graphic and pictorial portions of the Contract Documents showing the design, location and dimensions of the Work, generally including plans, elevations, sections, details, schedules and diagrams.

§ 1.1.6 The Specifications

The specifications are the portion of the Contract Documents consisting of the written requirements for materials, equipment, systems, standards and workmanship for the Work, and performance of related services.

§ 1.1.7 The Project Manual

The Project Manual is a volume assembled for the Work which may include the bidding requirements, sample forms, Conditions of the Contract and Specifications.

DRAWINGS

As stated in Chapter 11 – Project Phases, if you are working for an architect, your "engineering drawings" get started when the architect sends the CAD/BIM files of the building floor plans (shells) to you. When you are the prime professional, you start the drawings yourself.

When I first started my practice, we had to trace these shells on a light table to make our own "originals" (three times: once for power, then for low voltage, and again for lighting). We also had plenty of erasers handy for the inevitable changes. We thought we were getting high tech when we got an "electric eraser." In addition, each engineering discipline has additional sheets: legend, symbols, schedules, notes, 1-line diagrams, etc. Again, in my early days, these were all custom drawn by hand. Later, we used "stick-ons" (stand-pats). More and more information keeps getting added (and changed) until the drawings are finally complete.

Now, of course, we have CAD/BIM and fast computers to make the process more flexible and changeable. Each discipline/specialty has its own unique design and presentation methods and needs, which are beyond the scope of this book. But there are some commonalities to all the design specialties.

Drawing Recommendations

A Common Presentation

If each set of drawings prepared by a firm are arranged in the same order, it makes it easier for the trade contractors to bid. For example, I usually started out with the site electrical plan to give the electrical contractor an overall view of the project scope. Also, it is helpful to include a list of all your trade drawings on this same first sheet for the same reason. This is also a good place for the symbol legend. Next were the floor plans: lighting, power, and low voltage (grouped by area). Following this were the schedules, details, and notes. Most of the bidders separate the drawings into two sets: their trade and then everything else. They will appreciate a set organized in your "usual" way.

Standard Legend/Details/Schedules & 1-Lines

To be efficient, each office should develop standard details. When I was in practice, each member of the technical staff had a Standards Book (in a 3-ring binder). There was an index, and each item was numbered. Also, we each had access to a computerized version. As we developed this standards book, we had monthly "efficiency meetings." These meetings were limited to a ½ hour each, and assignments were made to develop or research proposed standards. Your firm will become more efficient if your staff doesn't individually "reinvent the wheel."

Office Record Drawings

Copies of all related addenda and change orders should be "cut out" and taped on to the appropriate page of the drawings. These "office record drawings" should be taken to the "punch list" site observation to avoid overlooking these official changes and clarifications. Also, note on this set any unofficial changes that you may have agreed upon with the contractor.

SPECIFICATIONS

As stated in Chapter 11 – Project Phases, the technical specifications are a written document that details the requirements of each of the items shown on the drawings. It specifies the requirements of something as (seemingly) simple as a light switch to something as complex as the functions of a fire alarm system. It also enumerates requirements for manufacturer's experience, workmanship, testing, and commissioning. This document is added at the end of the project manual by your architect client, unless you are the lead/prime professional, in which case the whole project manual is your responsibility.

Specification Questions

Usually, when the drawings are about 90% complete, it is time to prepare the technical specifications. I would meet with my project manager and review form **F-21** Electrical Specifications Checklist, which would have previously been completed. (See Chapter 13 – Operations Manual.) This list contains the basic information needed to organize and write the technical specifications. I recommend tailoring a document like this covering the items needed for the specifications of your discipline/specialty.

I usually wrote the specification myself after this meeting. It would probably be more efficient and accurate to provide a written instruction list and have your project manager actually prepare the project specifications. He is more aware of the project specifics, and errors will be avoided. However, writing the specification yourself is a good quality control (QC) check. Perhaps, carefully reviewing the Specifications Checklist with your project manager and later letting him prepare the specification might be the best solution.

Standard Specifications

I eventually had three (3) specifications versions:

- My standard one-section specification
- A modified multi-section MasterSpec Professional specification
- A modified multi-section MasterSpec Outline specification

My Standard One-Section Specification

My standard specification was all "one-section" and was the electrical specification that I received from my mentor, John W. King. I had modified it over the years, and it served me well. However, as AIA Standards recommended dividing divisions into more and more sections, architect/clients started asking for multiple electrical sections, especially on larger projects. So, I developed a multi-section specification. However, to my surprise, many architects complained that my specification (spec.) was too large. They often said, "It takes up about half of my project manual." Eventually, we used my "one-section" specification on more than half of our projects.

A Modified Multi-Section Masterspec Professional Specification

When I realized that I needed a multi-section specification, I investigated options available in the industry. I found that MasterSpec is sponsored by the AIA and was the most commonly used. I found it to be thoroughly researched, current, and in CSI Format, and it included tips and editing instructions, had great tech support, and one license covered the whole office location. They offer two versions: "Premium" – the longest version, and "Professional" – a shorter version. I felt that the Professional version met my needs.

A Modified Multi-Section MasterSpec Outline Specification

Occasionally, we were asked to provide an "Outline Specification" for a project. Sometimes, this was used to get preliminary pricing before the drawings were complete. Other times, this would be used as the final specification for a "design–build" project.

To be consistent, I, again, chose MasterSpec.

Specification Modifications

In modifying these masters, I first deleted materials and methods that I didn't like or didn't feel were appropriate for my geographical area of practice. Then, on an individual project basis, changes were made (for that project only) to suit the project needs and budget. For example, "wiring methods" were different for apartments, commercial buildings, and medical facilities.

However, the biggest change that I made was to add an "Electrical General Requirements" Section that included things like the following: (Note that this is a partial list)

Electrical General Requirements

- DESCRIPTION OF THE WORK
  - The work includes, but is not limited to, the following: (Insert list here)
- RELATED WORK SPECIFIED UNDER OTHER SECTIONS
  - Temporary wiring for building construction – see DIVISION 1
- MATERIALS FURNISHED BY OTHERS
- RELATED WORK BY OTHERS
- QUALITY ASSURANCE
  - Shop Drawings and Product Data required
- PERMITS AND FEES
- CODES AND STANDARDS
- ELECTRICAL INSTALLATION STANDARDS
  - NECA 1-2000 Standard Practices for Good Workmanship
- SCHEDULING AND SHUTDOWNS
- WORK INTERFERING WITH EXISTING WIRING
- REMOVALS AND RELOCATIONS
- PCB BALLAST REMOVAL
- CUTTING AND PATCHING

- CORE DRILLING
- SEALING
- ACCESS PANELS
- CHANGE ORDERS/PROPOSAL REQUESTS
- PACKAGED PRICING
- SITE OBSERVATIONS
- GUARANTEES/WARRANTIES
- SEISMIC RESTRAINTS – ELECTRICAL
- "LEED" COMMISSIONING
- UTILITY COORDINATION
- REBATE PROCEDURES
- AS-BUILT PREPARATION

Office Record Specifications

Like the "office record drawings," a copy of all related addenda and change orders should be "cut out" and taped on to the appropriate page of the specifications. These "office record specifications" should be taken to the "punch list site observation" to avoid overlooking these official changes and clarifications.

PROJECT MANUAL

For "private client projects" you will need to produce the entire project manual because you are the lead/prime professional. Therefore, you will need both bidding requirements and contract documents. The most commonly used are the ones produced by the AIA or the NSPE.

I immediately thought, "I'm an engineer; I should use NSPE standards." Fortunately, I asked around, and the president of one of the larger local engineering firms told me that when they started using the NSPE method, they got so many complaints from contractors that they changed to the AIA method. Basically, the contractors were already familiar with the AIA bidding conditions and contract documents and didn't want to learn another system. Also, many institutions (universities, hospitals, and municipalities) prefer the AIA documents.

Therefore, I used the AIA System.

- BIDDING REQUIREMENTS include Invitation to Bid, Bid Form, Letter of Intent, Supplementary Instructions to Bidders, Bid Bond, and Performance & Payment Bond.

- CONTRACT DOCUMENTS include Standard Form of Agreement, General Conditions, Supplementary Conditions, Special Conditions, and Schedule of Drawings.

Project Manual Inserts

The same information for the specific project gets inserted in many different places in both the project manual and in the client cover letter. To simplify your task, I recommend that you prepare a "Project Manual Insert Form" similar to Figure **14-1**. Also, modify both documents to contain the insert number. A secretary can easily insert the correct information where it belongs.

PROJECT MANUAL INSERTS

(Your Company Name Here)

Inserts – For "Master" Front End Of Specification

[1]   (Full title of project) (same as title block):

[2]   (Name, title, company name and address of clients representative):

[3]   (Address for receipt of bids):

[4]   (Address of Pre Bid Conference) (and specific room if appropriate):

[5]   (Name of owner) (company):

[6]   (Date of Spec) (month and year):

[7]   (Abbreviated name of Project) (for upper right hand corner):

[8]   (Place to pick up drawings and specifications):

[9]   (Name of Project Manager):

[10]   (Phone extension of our Project Manger):

[11]   (Name and phone number of client's representative):

FIGURE 14-1

OUTLINE SUMMARY

- **Common presentation:** Adopt "common drawing presentations" for all of your projects to make it easier for bidders to find things.

- **Standard details:** Implement "standard drawing details" to make your office more efficient.

- **Addenda & change orders:** Update your "office record drawings and record specifications" to include addenda and change orders.

- **Specifications questions:** Produce a list of "specification questions" to make specification writing easier and more accurate.

- **Three specifications:** Develop three specification versions: one-section, multi-section, and outline.

- **General requirements:** Add a general (specialty) requirements section to your specifications. Locate this near the beginning of your "one-section" specification and as a separate section in your "multi-section" specification.

- **Project manual:** Acquire a project manual for private client projects, including bidding requirements and contract documents.

- **Insert list:** Create a "Project Manual Insert List" to simplify preparing the project manual and the accompanying cover letter to the client.

CHAPTER 15

HUMAN RESOURCES

INTRODUCTION

Discover both the benefits and drawbacks of having employees and why you should grow your firm. Learn the inside scoop on finding experienced and easy-to-train technical help. Find out how to conduct an effective employment interview. Detect the art of making your offer "confidential." Observe how to foster loyalty and a family atmosphere. And last, but not least, uncover how to prevent a firing from backfiring.

GENERAL

The people who work for you are referred to as "human resources"; I just called them my staff. It is kind of like a marriage: "You can't live with them, but you can't live without them, either."

WHY HAVE HELP?

Benefits

- You are able to avoid "mundane" tasks (deliveries and fetching).
- You can assign tasks that you don't like to do.
- Clients object to paying your hourly rate for simple tasks.

- The lasting value of a "service" business is in the staff. *A mechanical engineer friend started his practice about the same time that I started mine. He made a good living, but he never had more than one drafter. When he retired, he laid off the drafter and closed the office. By the time that I retired, we had grown to a staff of eleven, and I had something valuable to sell.*

Drawbacks

- They don't get along with each other or, sometimes, with your clients.
- They often become your biggest deterrent to doing business.
- Dealing with their problems will consume more time than technical issues.
- As mentioned in Chapter 1, before you know it, you are responsible for thirty or more mouths to feed. That is an awesome and burdensome responsibility.

MY START

When my mentor retired, we had a draftsman who came with me when I opened my first office. Unfortunately, after a few weeks, I realized that I could not initially afford a staff and had to lay him off. I struggled alone for three years until I hired my first "project manager."

When I got my start, "staff" (human resources) were divided into three categories:

Project Managers (sometimes called a project designer)

Someone who could work from verbal instructions and design the "technical" (in my case electrical) portion of a project. He either drafted the drawings himself or marked them up for a drafter.

My first project manager had started in a large engineering firm a few years before as a drafter. He was a licensed electrician and had gradually learned the pieces of design until he could design all the electrical systems with the minimum of supervision. I had to pay him more than a drafter, but he could work on his own. It freed me up to meet with clients, do field investigations, write specifications, or do other engineering work while the projects were progressing.

Drafters

Someone who drew the plans (drawings) from markups (redlined prints). This included symbols, lines, and words on plans, schedules, legends, notes, details, and 1-line diagrams. This was done by hand working on a drafting table and using a straightedge, pencil, angles, and plastic symbol templates. For state highway work, we used lettering guides with ink on linen. As drafters gained knowledge, they could often work from verbal instructions. Most eventually became project managers.

Clerical

Receptionist, secretary, or bookkeeper.

Initially, we had no "clerical staff." My project manager answered the phone, I did the bookkeeping, and a local housewife typed letters and specifications, as needed.

Later, we were able to hire back my original drafter, who eventually became a good project manager.

GROWING PAINS

When the owner works in the same room with employees, the benefits include having a good grasp of what everyone is doing, knowing how they handle themselves on the phone and with visitors, hearing what questions that they ask, and knowing, in general, how each project is progressing. The drawbacks include your staff tending to ask you questions rather than making decisions on their own, you are constantly being interrupted, and they overhear (half of) every conversation that you have.

When you move to a private office, most of these problems are resolved, and a larger staff opens up new opportunities. But you become less aware of what is going on.

The staff liked to play tricks on my senior associate, whom they liked and was their direct supervisor. One time, they mounted his office door upside down. Another time, they hid his desk chair in the storage shed for three days. This was all good natured fun, and I didn't mind. It was good for moral. Another time, I discovered a new employee calling continually into a radio talk show trying to be caller #20 to win a prize. After that, radio talk shows were banned from our office.

TECHNOLOGICAL ADVANCEMENTS

Over time, new technology made the job easier and changed human resource needs. Soon, we were able to transfer details, notes, and schedules to new projects by "sticking them on" without redrawing. Eventually, CAD and BIM were developed, and now all the drawings are done electronically. Instead of tracing and revising the architect's shells, we are given electronic files. Mechanical drafters are no longer needed; CAD/BIM technicians are in demand. Project managers with CAD/BIM training have replaced many of the technicians.

Spell and grammar check have made the need for secretaries questionable. However, most engineers need more help than a computer can provide. Automated phone systems have replaced many receptionists.

POTENTIAL EMPLOYEES

I found that "salesmen" were the best source of leads for potential employees who were already working for my competitors.

I prepared a 3-ring binder. The first section listed all the engineering firms within a 40 mile radius along with the principals and key employees. The second section had a page for each potential candidate.

Each time that I needed a new employee, I met separately with the half dozen salesmen who regularly called on us, and I updated my binder, recording both positive and negative information. Be cautious because salesmen are motivated by their "self-interests"; they may be reluctant to recommend a good guy so that they can continue to be specified by both offices. Also, they may recommend an unqualified friend because his friend's present boss doesn't let him specify the salesmen's equipment.

Before contacting a potential employee, try to find out as much as you can about him. In addition, your staff may know him from past employment, engineering societies, or industry organizations. Also, those contractors on your selected bidder list may know him.

SCARCITY OF QUALIFIED TECHNICAL STAFF

As we grew, I stole trained project managers from my competition. But, eventually, the pool of good potential candidates dwindled. Usually, these people started as drafters and, over a number of years, gained electrical knowledge and design experience. The problem was that they usually didn't come from an electrical background and did not have the education and training in basic electricity and the National Electrical Code (NEC). Therefore, they had trouble adjusting to new technologies.

I started hiring licensed electricians; they understood electrical systems for buildings and the NEC. They were not confused when evaluating existing electrical conditions and were better able to coordinate with the local utility companies. When they went to project sites, they spoke the same language as the project electrician and were not easily misled. Also, many electricians were tired of being laid off and anxious to come in "out of the cold," so they were not unreceptive to the lower initial pay. Although these were not "engineers," they increased the professional standing of my staff and helped me to promote work from new clients and repeat work from satisfied clients. The fact that most of these new employees were in their thirties or forties added maturity to the staff. The one unexpected problem was getting them to work without talking about last night's ball game. But they soon learned that this job took more concentration than a repetitive task, like installing a light switch or junction box.

INTERVIEWS

I called potential employees personally to arrange for an interview. I tried to get their home phone number (or cell phone number) and called them after working hours.

When they arrived for the interview, my office manager sat them in the conference room to fill out our employment application. When the application was complete, we went into my office for the interview. After reviewing the application, I had a typed list of questions. Do not assume that because the applicant's title is "project manager" all the things that your project managers do are done. Question specifics. How much of the design do you do on his own? Do you attend meetings with the client? If yes, do you go alone? Do you write letters, conference memos, specifications, etc.? Also, ask how long the applicant has been doing each of these tasks. Take careful notes.

At some point, one of my clerical staff would enter carrying a tray with coffee, china cups, and a plate of cookies. This never failed to impress the applicant.

Tell the applicant that it is your policy to do a credit and background check on all potential employees. Ask if anything unusual will show up that they would like to explain. Make sure that you have a place on your employment application for them to sign authorizing both. I had a few people refuse to authorize this and they left before the interview. Great! This saves time and avoids a hiring mistake. With one background check, I received a copy of the applicant's "mug shot."

If the credit and background checks come back acceptable, a good last check is to call the candidate's "previous" employer (not his present employer). Tell the previous employer that you have heard good things about the candidate and are thinking of calling him in for an interview, but you wanted to get his opinion first. Some of the replies are just sour grapes, but others are enlightening.

THE OFFER

Once that you have decided to make an offer, call the candidate at home. Say that you are impressed and want to make an offer. Then, say, "But first, I want to tell you what I tell all prospective employees. You are, of course, free to discuss this offer with your significant other. But I want you to agree not to discuss it with your present employer or anyone else until you give me a definite answer. Is that acceptable to you?" If they don't agree, don't make an offer. If they do agree, repeat the condition one more time before making the offer. However, don't be shocked if they call you back and say, "My present employer has agreed to match your offer, and I have decided to stay."

HIRING MISTAKES

I have lost track of all the employees who came and went in my over 35 years of practice. Fortunately, most of my employees were terrific and did much to enhance the company's image and reputation. Unfortunately, not all of them were good hires.

I remember a project manager who was with me over six months and, seemingly, doing a fine job. He called me at home one morning at 6 am, waking me up. He told me that he was a CIA agent, his partner had been killed, and he was leaving on a 7 am flight to avenge the death and wasn't coming back. I have no idea what the real story was, but I wished him well.

Another fellow started out as a draftsman and left after about a year to work for one of my competitors. After a couple of years, he returned as a project manager. After a while, his work was so good that I assigned him as project manager on our largest, most important project. We discussed the project periodically, but I trusted him enough that I didn't yet review the drawings. When the project was reportedly 80% complete, I made an appointment with him to review the drawings and to write the specifications. He didn't show up for the meeting, quit, and would not return our calls. The job was in fact about 40% complete. I had to reassign the project, all of my staff had to put in overtime, the architect had to ask his client for a time extension, and we lost a lot of money on the project.

One of our repeat clients was a local university. One of their electrical engineers supervised several of our projects, and we got along well with him. So, when he approached me for a job, I didn't see much need to check him out any further. After about a week, I was told that he was making inappropriate comments, especially to the women. I spoke with the female staff. They could not refer to any direct threats, but they felt he was "creepy" and admitted they were afraid of him. I told him that it wasn't working out and I had to let him go. I found out later that the university couldn't fire him because "creepy" wasn't mentioned in their policy manual. They had a going away party when he left them, but they didn't invite him.

COMPANY NIGHT

Considering my operations manual and all its forms and form letters, it sounds like my firm was a pretty "rigid" place to work, and, in some respects, it was. I expected a lot from each employee. But I did my best to make it a pleasant work environment. I provided the coffee, and they were welcome to help themselves as frequently as they desired. I encouraged jokes and brief conversation during work as long as they were not distracting.

Every 2 or 3 months, I sponsored an outing after work. The whole staff would go to a bar for drinks and appetizers, a restaurant for dinner, or a pool hall for pool, drinks, and burgers. I did this so that we would all get to know each other in a social setting and, hopefully, create a "family" atmosphere in our office that would entice them to feel part of the group and want to stay. Consider an occasional "company night" at your firm.

One time, after the completion of a difficult and profitable project, I sponsored a cruise for my staff and their significant others. It was a "cruise to nowhere." It left from Boston (50 miles away) on a Friday afternoon and returned the following Sunday morning. I rented a fleet of limousines to take us from our office to the pier. We had a great time, and I feel that many friendships were cemented. Before returning by limousine to our office on Sunday, we had brunch at the Ritz Carlton in a beautiful ballroom overlooking the Boston Common.

It was a great 2 night cruise. Oddly enough, our cruise ship sunk the next week! Timing in life is somewhat by chance, but certainly is important.

Appreciate your staff, treat them like family, and they will be loyal and want to remain part of the clan.

FIRING IS HARDER THAN HIRING

The construction industry is "cyclical." It fluctuates with the economy.

When we had to lay someone off, I had a senior associate tell me (more than once) that an employee hadn't really worked out; after two years, he still worked at half the speed of the others. When I asked, "Why did we keep him this long?" he said, "Well, he was better than no one." On a very short-term basis, to meet a deadline, that might make sense, but to have this persist for two years defies logic. Don't assume that your #2 guy is going to tell you when you have some "dead wood." Conversely, make better hiring decisions than I did.

Whenever I let someone go, I tried to do it at the end of a work day. I had an "exit interview" form, and I usually said the reason was that "several projects that were about to start have been canceled." I paid them to the end of the week plus two weeks' severance pay. In addition, I offered them an additional two (or more) weeks' pay in return for signing a waiver agreeing that they had no grievance with the company and would not sue me or the company for any reason. If the departing employee was a project manager, I gave him a "project status" form for each of his projects and asked him to review his job folders and list any pending items. It was never fun, but I always did it personally. It was really difficult when they cried. But it was worse when they thanked me for the opportunity that I had given them.

OUTLINE SUMMARY

- **Benefits:** The benefits of having employees include avoiding mundane tasks and having clients objecting to paying your hourly rate for simple responsibilities. Also, the lasting value of a "service" business is in the staff.

- **Drawbacks:** The drawbacks of having employees include them not getting along with each other or, sometimes, with the clients, dealing with their problems, and being responsible for thirty or more mouths to feed—an awesome and burdensome responsibility.

- **Small size:** The benefits of being small include knowing what your staff are doing, seeing how they are developing, and being aware of how each project is progressing. The drawbacks of being small include too many questions/interruptions and your staff overhearing your conversations.

- **Growth:** The benefits of growth include privacy and increased opportunities. The drawbacks of growth include becoming less aware of what is going on.

- **Potential employees:** Recommendations for new employees come from salesmen, your existing employees, and contractors on your "Selected Bidder List." In addition, consider hiring tradesmen.

- **Interviews:** Invite potential employees to an interview when they are at home, develop an employment application and question list, and require a credit and background check.

- **The offer:** Try to require confidentiality when making an offer.

- **Company night:** Occasionally, socialize with your staff as a group outside the office; foster a "family" atmosphere and they will be loyal and want to remain part of the clan.

- **Firing is the hardest task:** Conduct an organized exit interview, pay severance, offer extra payment in return for signing a release, and have them fill out project status reports.

CHAPTER 16

FORENSIC ENGINEERING

INTRODUCTION

Understand what "forensic engineering" is and discover why this exciting, challenging, and profitable field should be part of your consulting engineering practice. Find out what is involved and if you have what it takes to be a success in the litigation arena.

You will learn how to prepare a curriculum vitae (CV), market your services, formulate a forensic fee agreement, conduct investigations, write reports, and prepare for depositions and the trial, including cross-examination.

WHAT IS FORENSIC ENGINEERING?

Forensic engineering is defined by the National Academy of Forensic Engineers (NAFE) as "the application of the art and science of engineering in matters which are in, or may possibly relate to, the jurisprudence system, inclusive of alternative dispute resolution." These engineers serve as consultants to the legal profession and as expert witnesses in courts of law.

SHOULD YOU CONSIDER THIS FIELD?

Benefits

- Interesting work

- Low liability
- High hourly rates
- Advanced payment via retainer
- Little competition

Drawbacks

- Can be stressful
- Sometimes requires travel

Because litigation consulting is interesting, challenging, and profitable, I recommend adding "forensic engineering" to your practice.

DO YOU HAVE WHAT IT TAKES?

To be an "expert witness," you don't need to be an engineer, but you do need experience and credentials in your field. To be an "engineering expert," you will usually need an engineering degree and a license as a professional engineer. In addition, being a member of NAFE is a big help in being selected and in assuring acceptance as an expert in court.

It is also important to have knowledge and qualifications in the engineering specialty involved in the particular case at hand. For example, if the issue is lighting or illumination, experience in lighting design and membership in the Illuminating Engineering Society of North America (IES) would be helpful. It's best to stick to your general area of expertise. If you are an electrical engineer, for instance, don't take on a civil engineering case.

In addition, you should possess the following general traits:

Speaking/Teaching Ability.

In court, you need to speak clearly, using proper English and making your statements and replies concise and easy to understand. You will be teaching the judge and jury your opinion of the case, and it is your job to convince them that you are correct.

Writing Skills.

Written reports need to be clear and professional. Don't put anything in writing until your attorney/client requests. Be sure you can defend every word under cross-examination.

Willingness to Prepare.

You are being paid to study the case and the technical issues involved. This can often be tedious, but it is the key to success. When preparing for court or deposition, it is crucial that you prepare for all possible questions and memorize much of the information.

Reading Skills.

In most cases, you will receive a box full of documents to review. These may include: (1) affidavits (written declaration of facts sworn to), (2) complaint (plaintiff's initial pleadings), (3) depositions (oral testimony taken by the opposing attorney in advance of trial), (4) indictments (written accusations presented by a grand jury), (5) interrogatories (written questions sent to the opposing side and written answers submitted under oath), (6) petitions (written applications to the court requesting judicial action), (7) pleadings (written statements of contentions of the parties in the suit), (8) subpoenas (written orders for witnesses to appear), (9) summons (writ directing an officer to notify a defendant to appear in court), and (10) transcripts (official record of proceedings in a trial, deposition, or hearing).

It is part of your job to read all of these documents and to cull the information pertinent to your involvement in the case. This can mean many hours of reading even though many of these documents have no bearing on your portion of the case.

WHAT IS INVOLVED?

Cases include some, or all, of the following: site investigation, examination and testing of evidence, reports (verbal, summary, and detailed), testimony at deposition, and testimony at trial (direct and cross-examination).

There are two sides to every case. The person who brings the action is the "plaintiff." If you work for his or her attorney, you are a plaintiff's witness. The other party in the suit is the "defendant." If you work for his or her attorney, you are a defendant's witness. In your forensic practice, you will almost exclusively be involved with civil cases (noncriminal matters).

There are two types of witnesses: a "fact witness" and an "expert witness." A fact witness can only tell what he or she observed, not what others have said (hearsay) and not his or her opinion concerning the case. You, however, will be an expert witness (a technical witness), and, as such, you are allowed to express your opinions on matters within your expertise.

The attorney who hires you may represent the plaintiff, the defendant, or their insurance companies. When you work directly for an attorney, your work is protected from discovery (detection) by the opposition because it is "attorney work product." Avoid working directly for the parties of the suit because your work is not similarly protected.

As you will see later in this chapter, your "scope of services" in your forensic fee agreement is important. The words "Consultant and (if designated) expert" allows your attorney/client to deny that you were dismissed as an expert witness if he or she doesn't like your opinion as a consultant.

Above all, you must be truthful at all times. You must be supportive of your opinion without arguing for your attorney/client. Your opinion will not always coincide with that of your attorney/client. His or her job is to advocate for the client. Your job is to form an accurate and scientifically consistent opinion and to convey that to your attorney/client. If your attorney/client doesn't agree with your theory of the case, he or she can get another expert. In addition, he or she can benefit from your contrary opinion because your findings will point out the weaknesses in their case and may prompt a settlement.

CURRICULUM VITAE (CV)

Your CV is what your expert witness resume is called. The more detailed and complete it is, the more qualified you will appear.

Include the following items:

- Specialty – Summary of your area of expertise.
- Education – Starting with college and including degrees and honors, post-graduate studies, and certifications.
- Professional registrations – List states and numbers.
- Professional practice – Present and previous company affiliations, positions, and titles.
- Professional affiliations – Memberships in professional/technical groups and offices held.

- Honors and awards – List name of honor/award and group presenting it.
- Publications – List title, publication, and month and year.
- Lectures – List title, group presented to, and month and year.
- Forensic activities – List the most recent first, including:
  - Title (example) LIGHTNING INVESTIGATION, Westerly, RI.
  - Date hired.
  - Your job number.
  - Parties to the case and official court case number and venue.
  - Retaining attorney (also list if for defense or plaintiff).
  - Synopsis: Two brief paragraphs, the first describing the incident and the second describing your assignment, including whether it involved deposition and/or testimony at trial.

Print your CV on your stationary (letterhead for the first page and second sheet for the others) and bind it between covers embossed with your company name. See Figure **16-1** for the first few pages of my CV.

CV EXAMPLE (1 OF 4)

(Example of Forensic CV)

JOHN D. GASKELL, P.E.

Specialty: ELECTRICAL SYSTEMS FOR BUILDINGS

(Forensic consulting electrical engineer specializing in disputes relating to Electrical design and construction of buildings: Electrical failures/explosions; electrocutions; fires of electrical origin; errors and omissions; standard of care; National Electrical Code compliance; illumination evaluations; power quality; grounding; lightning protection; and electrical accidents. Member: National Academy of Forensic Engineers.)

Education: Bachelor of Science in Electrical Engineering
University of Rhode Island, 1966

Associates in Electrical Engineering Technology
Wentworth Institute, Boston, MA 1962

Professional Registration:

Registered Professional Engineer in Massachusetts and Connecticut.

Professional Practice:

John D. Gaskell, P.E. is president of Gaskell Associates Consulting Electrical Engineers. This engineering practice, established by him in 1971, specializes in electrical systems for buildings. Gaskell Associates is a division of Thielsch Engineering, a 250 person, diverse engineering firm.

For over 30 years Gaskell Associates has provided electrical design services to architects and building owners, including: Power Distribution Systems; Emergency Power systems; High voltage Power Distribution systems; Lighting Design; Fire alarm systems; Lightning Protection Systems; Security alarm Systems; communications systems; MATV & CCTV Systems; Computer Power and Network Systems; UPS & Power Conditioning Systems; Magnetic Field Measurements and Mitigation; Power Quality Studies, Measurements and Monitoring; Feasibility Studies and Forensic Investigations & Legal Testimony.

Service to clients has been the key to their success.

FIGURE 16-1

CV EXAMPLE (2 OF 4)

(Example of Forensic CV)

Professional Affiliations:

National Society of Professional Engineers (NSPE)

President of the Rhode Island Society of Professional Engineers 1980-1981

Illuminating Engineering Society of North America (IESNA)

Founding President of the Rhode Island Chapter 1975-1976

National Academy of Forensic Engineers

R.I. State Building Code Standards Committee (Past Member)

Electrical Sub-committee Past Chairman

Electrical League of Rhode Island

Providence Engineering Society

National Electromagnetic Field Testing Association

Honors and Awards:

FREEMAN AWARD from the Providence Engineering Society

This award was established for the purpose of recognizing major achievement in engineering. It is held to be unique in that it recognizes accomplishment, inventiveness, development of theory, or the application of scientific knowledge in such a way as to provide advancement in the art and practice of engineering.

ENGINEER OF THE YEAR

From the Rhode Island Society of Professional Engineers

LIGHTING DESIGN AWARDS

Hall Library, Cranston, Rhode Island
From the New England Section of IESNA

Lincoln School Gym, Providence, Rhode Island
From the Rhode Island Chapter of IESNA

ESD FIRST PLACE NATIONAL DESIGN AWARD

"UNINTERRUPTIBLE Power Supply" (UPS) system for Fleet National Bank's Computer Operations Center in Providence, RI, with initial capacity of 600 KVA and expandable to 1 Megawatt.
From Electrical Systems Design Magazine

FIGURE 16-1

CV EXAMPLE (3 OF 4)

(Example of Forensic CV))

WEISMAN MEMORIAL AWARD

In recognition of sustained and meritorious service
From the Rhode Island chapter of IESNA

MAN OF THE YEAR

From the Electrical League of Rhode Island

Publications:

"Anatomy of a Power Outage." Electrical Construction & Maintenance (EC&M) Magazine, October 2001

"Consulting Engineer: Watch Out for Decline in Power Quality." APC UPTIME, April 2001

"Avoiding EMF's – Designing Buildings Limiting Occupants Exposure to EMF's." Power Quality Assurance, September/October 1996

"Electrical Design with EMF in Mind." Electrical Construction & Maintenance (EC & M) Magazine, February 1995

"Expandable UPS Serves Bank Operations Center." Electrical Construction & Maintenance (EC & M) Magazine, March 1988

"Effects of Voltage Reduction." Electrical Consultant, February 1974

Lectures:

"How Fire Alarm System Requirements Affect Building Owners." Lecture presented to the Building Owners and Managers Association of Rhode Island, May 2005.

"What Realtors need to know about the New Fire alarm Systems Requirements." Lecture presented to the Rhode Island Association of Realtors, February 2005.

"Fire Alarm Systems for Building Owners." Seminar presented by Gaskell Associates Consulting Engineers to over 400 attendees regarding the changes to the Rhode Island Fire Safety Code precipitated by the 2003 Station Nightclub Fire, November 2004.

"Electrical Systems for Buildings." Lecture presented at the advanced lighting course for the Rhode Island Chapter of the Illuminating Engineering Society of North America, January 2000.

"Power Quality Audits and Monitoring." Lecture presented at the Rhode Island Plant Engineering Maintenance Show and Conference, October 1999.

"Forensic Engineering – How to prepare a case." Lecture presented at the Rhode Island Plant Engineering Maintenance Show and Conference, October 1999.

"Power Quality Studies and Monitoring." Lecture presented to the Southern New England Network Users Group, July 1998.

FIGURE 16-1

CV EXAMPLE (4 OF 4)

(Example of Forensic CV)

"Power Quality in New Buildings." Lecture presented at the Building Systems Course, Roger Williams University, Bristol, RI, April 1998.

"Electrical Systems for Buildings." Lecture presented at the advanced lighting course for the Rhode Island Chapter of the Illuminating Engineering Society of North America, January 1998.

"Power Quality – Why be concerned." Lecture presented to AIA Rhode Island, a chapter of the American Institute of Architects, November 1997.

"Forensic Engineering." Lecture presented to the Rhode Island Chapter of the Illuminating Engineering Society of North America, November 1997.

"Power Quality Audits." Lecture presented to the New England Healthcare Engineers Society at their Fall Seminar in New London, Connecticut, November 1996.

"The Industrial Design Building @ 161 South Main Street." Lecture at the Rhode Island School of Design (RISD), October 1996.

"Power Quality Studies & Solutions." Lecture presented to the Rhode Island Chapter of the American Association of Plant Engineers, October 1996.

"Avoiding EMF's." Lecture presented at the National Conference on Harmonics and Power Quality in Philadelphia, Pennsylvania, May 1995.

"The Architect's Role in Electrical Design." Lecture presented at the Rhode Island School of Design (RISD), October 1994 and December 1995.

"Lighting Design in Commercial Buildings." Lecture presented at Roger Williams University College of Architecture, September 1992.

"I.E.S. Lighting Design Awards." Lecture presented to the Rhode Island Chapter of the American Institute of Architects at their Fall Conference, October 1990.

"Uninterruptible Power Supply Systems." Lecture presented to the Rhode Island Hospital Engineers Association, February 1987.

"Energy Efficiency in Electrical Systems." Lecture presented for the Rhode Island Chapter of the American Association of Plant Engineers, March 1986.

"Electrical Systems for Buildings." Course presented at Roger Williams University College of Engineering, fall 1982, 1983 and 1984.

"IES Introduction to Light and Lighting." Course for the Rhode Island Chapter of IES, Spring 1978.

FIGURE 16-1

MARKETING YOUR FORENSIC ENGINEERING SERVICES

Much of the advice in Chapters 9 and 10 on marketing apply here.

When I decided to make forensic engineering a significant portion of my practice, I prepared an elaborate single piece, foldout, full color brochure. I had a friend, an official at a nearby courthouse, who arranged for me to use a courtroom for pictures by a professional photographer. I mailed my new advertising piece for review to someone who is highly regarded as an expert with much litigation experience. He thought my forensic brochure was too showy and unprofessional, and I never used it.

Instead of making the mistake that I did, I recommend you send your CV to litigation attorneys in your area with a cover letter introducing yourself. Ask them to put it in their expert witness file, and request that they keep you in mind for appropriate cases.

It is also recommended that you join the National Academy of Forensic Engineers (NAFE). They are affiliated with the National Society of Professional Engineers and are a charter member of the Council of Engineering Specialty Boards. Through their accreditation process and requirements for continuing professional development, each member of the Academy is a Board Certified Diplomat in Forensic Engineering. There are three levels of membership: member, senior member, and fellow. Membership requirements are stringent, including, at the member level, testimony under oath in at least two cases. Check out the full qualifications online, and join as soon as you qualify. The NAFE Directory is published on CD and distributed to all members. Many referrals are made from this data. Become affiliated as a correspondent until you are eligible for membership.

Another source of forensic work is companies who frequently hire experts in your field. For example, if you are an electrical consulting engineer, use your contacts at the local power companies to find out which attorneys help them to defend against law suits.

There are also expert directories where you can pay to be listed. I have never tried them, but some engineers report good results.

Often, one of the participants to a suit is an insurance company which may need an expert witness with your specialty. Many of their attorneys are "in house" (employees). Contacting appropriate insurance companies may be fruitful.

Avoid "conflicts of interest." If you reject a case after reviewing nonpublic information from one side, it is not ethical for you to work for the other side. On the other hand, if you only reviewed public information, you are not prohibited from working for the opposition. It is often a good policy to work for whichever party calls first. Occasionally, if you are in a very specialized field, an attorney may hire you having no plan to give you any billable hours just to keep his opposition from hiring you. Your nonrefundable retainer should be high enough to discourage this practice.

FORENSIC FEE AGREEMENT

See Figure **16-2** for an example of a Forensic Fee Agreement. Most of these items are self-explanatory. Modify, as needed. You should also note the following:

The "scope of services" is important. You will be a consultant until after you reach an opinion consistent with your retaining attorney. At that point, you are usually designated as one of his expert witnesses. If he doesn't like your opinion (as a consultant), he can deny that he dismissed you as an expert witness.

Don't start working on the case until you receive the signed agreement and the retainer check. I usually eliminate the retainer requirement for insurance companies as I generally consider them "credit worthy."

Instead of using my fee agreement, you may want to consider the SEAK Expert Witness Retention Contract. I have been told that a large number of experts use it and that it is well accepted by attorneys, despite offering fair and favorable terms for the expert. It is available for download on the website http://www.seak.com, for a fee.

FORENSIC FEE AGREEMENT

(Your company Letterhead)

CASE: _____

SCOPE OF SERVICES: Electrical Consultant and (if desired) as Expert _____

SERVICES & EXPENSES

Personnel	Rate per Hour
Forensic Engineer	$XXX
Forensic Investigator (2)	$XXX
Technician	$XXX

Expenses	Rate
Travel (3)	At cost
Mileage	$0.XX per mile
Out of Pocket Expenses	At cost

(1) Rates indicated are for all services, including travel. A minimum of eight hours per day is charged for attendance/waiting/testimony at any deposition, trial or hearing, regardless of location, and regardless of any delays or rescheduling, and shall not be contingent on actual testimony or testimonial qualifications. For depositions we will provide you with a separate statement with which to bill the deposing attorney for re-imbursement.

(2) A Forensic Investigator is a non-P.E. who will assist the chief investigator (expert witness) with investigations.

(3) Travel expenses include car rental, taxi, meals, business class hotel and coach class air travel. Travel arrangements and lodging selections are subject to approval by us.

TERMS

- Services are subject to availability.

- To retain us, please send $X,XXX to establish a Retainer fund, which sum, exclusive of any expenses, shall constitute our minimum professional fee for availability to you in this matter. Our hourly fee, billed in one-half segments, and any expenses shall be drawn from the Retainer fund as work is completed.

- Periodic detailed billing statements are rendered, usually monthly, and are due immediately upon receipt. Outstanding balances past due over thirty days are subject to a delinquency charge of xx percent per month until paid. (Insert your company name here), with liability, may withhold delivery of reports and other data and may suspend performance of its obligations to Client pending full payment of all charges.

- In order to schedule our deposition or trial/hearing testimony (regardless of location), or any out of state travel, all payments must be current and advance payment must be received for all expenses plus fees for time anticipated.

- The laws governing this contract shall be those of the State of (insert your state) and the venue and jurisdiction of this contract is the county of (insert your county). You agree to be responsible for all attorney fees, costs, expenses, and interest relating to the collection and enforcement of this contract.

- In retaining us, not withstanding any relationship you may have with third parties, contingency arrangements, subrogation, etc., you, as our client, agree to be liable for and to pay us for any and all services rendered and expenses incurred, including any fees or costs incurred by our response to discovery efforts of others. Terms on outstanding balances are net 30 days.

- The client (and subsidiaries of the client) agree not to attempt to hire (or discuss employment with) any employees (or former employees) of (insert your company name), until one year has passed, since their employment by us.

- We guarantee that we will use our best efforts on your behalf; however, we do not promise or guarantee what our eventual opinions will be, nor what effect our work will have, on the outcome of the case. Our conclusions will be based, in part, on the accuracy and completeness of the information you provide.

These fees and provisions are hereby agreed to by the undersigned parties.

_____
Insert Your Company Name

Authorized Signature: _____

Printed Name & Title: _____
Address: _____
_____
_____

Dated: _____

Dated: _____

FIGURE 16-2

INVESTIGATIONS

The more investigation, research, analysis, and testing that you do, the more credible and convincing your testimony will be. Your investigation will, of course, depend on the details of the issues in your field of involvement. Your attorney/client can arrange access to evidence or the site. Do not rely on your memory; take detailed notes.

Site Investigation

If appropriate, visit the site to see the actual circumstances of the incident. Besides a pad and pen, bring a camera and possibly binoculars. Take many pictures and make sketches, if appropriate. Try to determine if the conditions now are the same as they were immediately following the incident.

One of my first investigations was of a fire of suspected electrical origin. The fire damage was extensive, with insulation melted off of much of the exposed wiring in the basement. Many of the covers were missing from junction boxes, and some had wiring hanging out with connections exposed without wire nuts. I documented all of these violations and thought, "No wonder the place burned down." It wasn't until I was driving home that it dawned on me that there were probably a half-dozen investigators there before me who created most of the violations. Don't assume that things were always as you find them.

Be prepared to interview persons who may be able to offer useful information. It would be helpful to bring a tape recorder for interviews or to simplify note-taking.

Examination

If applicable, relevant items may be sent to you or you may have to go somewhere else to view, examine, and possibly test them. Besides a pad and pen, bring a camera and surgical gloves. Before touching these items, explain to representatives of both parties what you plan to do, how you plan to do it, and receive permission before proceeding. Take many pictures and make sketches, if appropriate. Depending upon the magnitude of the case, there may be a dozen or more people present, and you may have to wait your turn.

If you suspect that evidence has been tampered with or spoiled, immediately inform your attorney/client.

Testing

Consider pertinent testing, if needed. In some cases, this is your responsibility; in others, testing should be done by an independent laboratory. One argument for independent testing may be that you don't have the required measuring devices; another is that independent tests appear more objective. Have your attorney/client contract directly with the laboratory so the lab results will be his work product. If you do the testing, it is usually best to rent the test equipment and have the supplier provide a report of recent calibration and accuracy of the instrument. You don't want to be questioned about these issues regarding your meters while on the witness stand. Review, advise your attorney/client, and obtain written permission before proceeding. I wouldn't hesitate to proceed, however, if your attorney/client is present, informs you that the other side has approved, and is aware of what you will do.

There are two types of testing: nondestructive and destructive. Do only nondestructive testing on the actual item that is the issue of the action. If the testing needs to be destructive, obtain an "exemplar," an identical item. There may be others at the site or an exact copy may be available from the manufacturer. In any case, get permission before testing of any kind.

Sometimes, it is appropriate for you to observe testing by others. Also, you or someone else may be asked to write a "protocol" (procedure) for testing for approval by all parties prior to testing.

WHITE PAPERS

To properly prepare your case, it is often necessary to research specialized areas of your field, such as those that may be new to you or you haven't needed since college. While doing this studying, make notes in a narrative form to make it easier for you to write your later report. In addition, these notes will help you prepare for your deposition and for trial as an expert. These papers prepare you for cross-examination questions on the specialized technical area at issue. They have the added advantage of preparing you for questions in the general technical area but not specific to this case.

These are often called "white papers," a compilation of your knowledge on a specific topic. It organizes your research for use on future cases. If the source information is paraphrased, it could also be the basis for a magazine article authored by you. As stated previously, reprints will help you earn a reputation as an expert in your field.

YOUR CASE FILE

Your case file is discoverable by the opposition. Be very careful what it includes. Keep written correspondence to a minimum. Your theory of the case may evolve and change over time as you uncover more information. The first two pages should be your case summary and case time and charges.

On the case summary sheet, add a narrative of the case: who, what, when, and where the incident (accident, failure, fire, explosion, error, etc.) occurred, including basic facts, events, injuries, sources, and weather, if pertinent. Update your ongoing summary of your investigation and possibly include proposed future actions and questions. Avoid unfounded accusations. As your forensic engineering practice grows, it may become harder to remember the status of each case. Also, priorities change and some cases go on hold for extended periods. If an attorney/client calls about his or her case and you don't remember the details, say you are in conference and will return the call later. Find the case file, read the summary, and return his call. Prepare this record on your computer so that, as it is updated, there is no record of changes.

Each time that you work on a case, indicate the date and the start and stop times on the case time and charges sheet. When you are interrupted by an unrelated activity, be sure to subtract that time from your sheet. At the end of each month, send a bill for your time. Include a summary of activity for the month, listing the day and the total time for the day rounded up to quarter- or half-hours. Do not break down the time for each task.

REPORTS

Do not write reports until your attorney/client requests. There are three basic types of reports: verbal, summary, and detailed.

Verbal Reports

Preliminary reports should be oral because the investigation is ongoing and not all questions have been answered. Also, your attorney/client doesn't want your opinion committed to writing until he or she knows what it is. Tell your attorney/client both the strengths and weaknesses and the status of your investigation.

Call your attorney/client as soon as you find serious flaws in his or her side of the case.

Summary Written Report

After your verbal report, your attorney/client may request a summary report. Be sure that you review exactly the depth that he or she wants before proceeding. Usually, this type of report is requested if the case is expected to go to trial and your attorney/client does not want to give away your full position.

Detailed Written Report

Instead, after your verbal report, your attorney/client may request a detailed report. Again, be sure to review exactly the depth he or she wants before proceeding. Usually, this type of report is requested if the case is expected to settle and the strategy is to reveal how strong your arguments are, thus encouraging a settlement.

Before writing your report, ask your attorney/client for a written guide outlining the case strategy, desired testimony, and questions to be answered. In my experience, you will be lucky to get an off-the-top-of-the-head verbal response.

Regardless of length, reports should be organized in the following manner:

Begin with a summary of the background of the case. Include the "who, what, when, and where" of the incident (accident, failure, fire, explosion, error, etc.). Include basic facts, events, injuries, sources, and weather, if pertinent. You should already have this information on your case summary sheet.

Next, describe your investigation. Include a list of documents read, interviews held, site observations, tests conducted or observed (including a summary of the results), and a laboratory test result summary.

Include an opinions section. It is best to state each opinion separately, including the justifications for each. Be sure you can substantiate each word in each opinion because you may be extensively cross-examined. Be sure this section is complete because these are the only opinions to which you will be allowed to testify, unless new information becomes available.

Attach an appendix to your report, including test reports, sketches, and photographs with a caption on each explaining what it depicts and its relevance. The appendix should include a list of reference materials (textbooks, handbooks, and published papers) supporting your findings. Be thorough and include page numbers from all sources.

THE DEPOSITION

Depositions (oral testimony, under oath, taken by the opposing attorney in advance of trial) are often required of expert witnesses, especially if the case is expected to go to trial.

If you are to be deposed, your attorney/client will usually call you to set up an appointment. However, don't be surprised if a sheriff shows up at your home or office with a subpoena. Just notify your attorney/client. Be sure to ask what to bring. Usually, you will bring your CV and your report, if any. Don't bring your folder unless directed to do so. If you do bring it, be prepared that the opposing attorney might make a copy of it, which he or she has every right to do.

The main purpose of the deposition is "discovery" —learning what you know regarding the case, including your findings and opinions. Keep your answers brief and do not deviate from the questions. Be prepared: Reread your report or summary of the case, and memorize important facts, including names, places, and dates. Be prepared to recite a narrative of the case from memory. Practice listing your findings and opinions just as you may have to do in court. Anticipate questions and prepare answers. During the deposition, listen carefully; a slightly different question may require a very different answer.

Another purpose of the deposition might be to gather information for impeachment, which is an attack on your credibility. Your credentials, reputation, or personal history may be challenged. Know your CV well enough that you can easily summarize it from memory. (If you have a checkered past, this may not be the right line of work for you.) The second way to impeach an expert witness is to discredit his or her opinions. Make sure your opinions are based on science or standards that are general accepted in your field of expertise. Don't say, "The high voltage line was dangerously close to the building." Instead, say, "The 12,000 volt power line was 8 feet from the building, while the National Electrical Safety Code, at the time of installation, required a minimum of 10 feet, thus creating a hazard." Be specific and able to substantiate each word of every statement. State each opinion separately and with enough information that it can stand on its own.

Generally, there is no time limit on depositions; one to three hours is normal. *I attended one deposition that took more than six hours. The parking garage had closed, and I had to take a cab home and come back for my car the next day.*

Make sure your fee agreement clearly clarifies your compensation for depositions. Don't let your payment be dependent on reimbursement by the deposing attorney.

THE TRIAL

The good news is that the vast majority of cases settle; the bad news is that you need to prepare every case as if it will go to trial.

Review what to bring to court with your attorney/client. Usually, bring the following:

- Your CV. Be prepared to present it orally from memory. Summarize your cases by saying something like, "I have been involved with 18 cases as an expert witness. I was deposed in 10 of them, and I testified at trial 4 times."
- Your fee schedule, time sheets, bills, and case summary. Make sure that these records are up to date and be prepared to answer the question, "How much time did you spend on this case and what were your total charges to date?"
- Your report. Again, be prepared to present it orally from memory.

Don't bring your case file unless directed to do so. If you do bring it, carefully remove any irrelevant, early, or incorrect information.

Preparation for trial is similar to that needed for a deposition. The important difference is how clearly and convincingly you present your opinions. Juries tend to believe expert witnesses who appear confident, knowledgeable, and likable.

Another difference is the thoroughness of your preparation. Write out questions and detailed answers. These should each be concise. Juries lose their train of thought with run-on questions or answers; break them up into smaller pieces. Group them by topic and in appropriate order. For example: site investigation, interviews, examinations/observations, tests, and opinions. Also, include broad enquiries: "Tell us about all of your opinions and the justification for each. When did you first form that opinion?" (Hopefully it was not before you knew the results of your investigation.) Send them to your attorney/client for review. Also, ask him or her to send you a written list of other possible questions.

Practice aloud in front of a mirror until you can recite the answers from memory with conviction and without "umms" and "I thinks." This will adequately prepare you for your direct examination by your attorney/client.

Next, try to predict questions the opposing attorney might ask during his or her cross-examination. The opposing expert's report will be an inspiration for possible questions. Try to craft an appropriate response to each, answers that don't sound defensive. Try to find out the name of the attorney who is expected to cross-examine you so you can address him or her by last name in court. If you forget the name, address the attorney as "counselor."

In some cases, exhibits are effective. If you think of a prop that illustrates your opinions and makes them easier to understand, review that with your attorney/client well ahead of time.

On the day of court, arrive early and well rested. Men should wear a suit or conservative jacket and tie. A dark pinstriped suit, bow tie, and pocket square worked for me; it might not be best for you. Most women look impressive in a dark-colored suit, neutral blouse, and medium-heeled pumps. Don't show up in casual or sporty clothes.

Don't let the unexpected throw you off of your game. Try to picture in your mind, ahead of time, whom and what you may see in court. If someone was terribly disfigured in a fire, be prepared for the encounter. If someone injured his right hand in the accident, be prepared for him to offer his left hand for a handshake.

As you approach the witness stand, give a copy of your business card to the court reporter. He or she will spell your name correctly, and the jury will believe this is not your first testimony.

While on the stand, sit up straight and lean slightly forward to give the appearance of full attention. Respond confidently to each question, and address your reply to the jury, looking directly at them. Your attorney/client will do your direct examination, and the first questions will be to qualify you as an expert witness. Beforehand, discuss with your attorney/client regarding the depth that he desires, and be prepared to recite your qualifications from memory. Oftentimes, if your qualifications are eminent, the opposing attorney will "stipulate" to your qualifications: accept you as an expert without enumeration. Sometimes, my attorney/client objected to stipulation; he wanted the jury to hear my qualifications. Appear calm at all times, and try not to let the opposing attorney get you visibly upset.

Remember that you should not express opinions on matters beyond your expertise. Respond as follows: "I am not qualified as an expert in that area of expertise." If your answer to a question is "I don't know," and the opposing attorney presses you further, look at the judge and state, "I don't want to guess."

Regardless of how you think you did, leave the stand walking erect with your head held high and a neutral expression on your face.

CROSS-EXAMINATION

In my experience, most opposing attorneys are civilized. However, some of them can be nasty and abrupt in their cross-examinations. Consider questions like the following, and craft answers that suit your personality and temperament. But listen carefully because a slightly differently worded question may require an entirely different reply. After every question, pause for a beat to give yourself time to form the best answer and to allow your attorney/client time to object. If he or she does object, immediately stop talking until the judge rules. In any case, try not to lose your cool.

Question: How much are you being paid for your testimony?

Answer: *My company charges $xxx per hour for my professional services; my testimony is not for sale.*

Question: Isn't it true that you would not be here today if it weren't for the obscene amount of money that you are being paid?

Answer: *Like you, counselor, I am being paid appropriately for my professional services.*

Question: Have you ever lied?

Answer: *Of course, but never under oath.*

Question: Have you ever been wrong?

Answer: *Yes, but never on the witness stand.*

Question: Did you read all the documents regarding this case?

Answer: *I requested all of the relevant documents and read them.*

Question: You haven't told us everything today, have you?

Answer: *No, it would be impossible to condense 40 years of professional practice into a few hours.*

Question: What is the reputation of the opposing expert?

Answer: *I like him. I don't know what others think of him.*

Question: Did you remove any information from your case file?

Answer: *I updated my case file, but I didn't remove any relevant information.*

Question: How much money do you make in an average year?

Answer: *That is personal and not relevant to these proceedings.*

If you are directed by the judge to answer, respond with one of the following:

Answer: *My income from litigation related services is about $xx,xxx.*

or

I don't know; it varies from year to year.

Question: Did your attorney/client tell you what to say today?
Answer: *No, of course not. Except to speak slowly and clearly.*

Be especially cautious of compound questions, run-on multiple questions, or ones with multiple parts. Ask to have them rephrased, one question at a time. Politely keep asking for clarifications until you understand the question.

CASES

When I first started my practice, I was the new kid and didn't get calls for this type of work. Later, as my staff grew, I needed to spend most of my time supervising and managing the business, so I didn't pursue forensic investigations.

Accept only cases in your field of expertise, but don't necessarily limit them to your area of specialty. My cases as an electrical engineer included electrocutions, fires of suspected electrical origin, standard of care determinations, equipment failures, arc fault accidents, conveyor accidents, lightning strikes, and others. Yours will be different but also interesting and challenging. I wish you much success in the exciting field of forensic engineering.

CASE STUDIES

The following are narrative synopses of a few of my cases. This is not intended to be a formal presentation of legal actions. No confidential or privileged information is revealed. They are simply my recollections, intended only to illustrate an expert's typical involvement in judicial matters.

I was the chief investigator and expert witness on all of the forensic cases of Gaskell Associates, Ltd., and later those of the Gaskell Associates division of Thielsch Engineering until my retirement. However, it was my practice to meet on each case with my senior staff to "brainstorm" the case. This often opened up avenues of investigation that had not previously occurred to me. Gary Hebner was a licensed electrician and served as lead investigator on many of my cases. (I attribute much of my success to hiring others who are smarter than I am.)

Case Study #1 – Lightning Strike

My first "forensic" case involved injury by lightning. It was so long ago that I don't remember if the event was fatal or not. An employee at a factory was told that it was raining and her car windows were open. She borrowed an umbrella and walked to her car. At some point, she was struck by lightning. I wasn't called in until more than a year later, when the case was about to go to court. My job was to visit the site and measure distances from the point of the incident to structures (fence, poles, and buildings) and associated heights. I examined what was left of the umbrella, reviewed the weather report for the day, and studied lightning theory. Eventually, I testified as an expert witness for the plaintiff at trial regarding what occurred. I didn't know enough to charge more than my usual hourly rate, but I was impressed that I could get paid to study an interesting topic like lightning.

Case Study #2 – Power Line Height

During the early 1990s, the architectural, engineering, and construction industry went into a deep recession, and I needed to personally produce billable hours. I started taking on "forensic" cases for the local power company's attorneys. Most of these cases involved whether or not power lines were an adequate distance from a structure. The code involved here is the National Electrical Safety Code (NESC). The determination of proper distances was complex because it depended on the date of installation and the version of the code that was in effect at the time. I was already considered an expert on the National Electrical Code (NEC), and I soon became an expert on the NESC, which lead to more cases.

One of my first cases involved a power line that crossed a state highway and was torn down by a passing truck. This incident had occurred two years prior, and my first thought was: "How can I figure out the height of a line that is no longer in place?" But, although it had been dragged for a half-mile, they had salvaged the line and attachments, and the two associated poles were still in place. I visited the site with a land surveyor and recorded the distances, heights of attachments, and crown of the road. Because of the difficulty of shutting down the highway, we attempted to reconstruct the line in a field that had a pole. We hoisted the other end with a bucket truck, measured the low point of the line, and adjusted for the crown of the highway. So far, I hadn't used any of my "electrical engineering" skills, but I learned that ingenuity and common sense can often lead to a solution.

Case Study #3 – Power Line Proximity to Structure

An interesting case involved "Ozzie" the roofer. Part of my job was to read his "deposition," his fact witness statement of what he observed. Ozzie was hired to put a new rubber roof on a tenement. Near the completion of the project, he was attaching the 10-foot metal edge strips. As he was nailing a strip to the edge, he saw another strip start to blow off the roof and reached out to grab it. In doing so, he extended it out into contact with a 25,000 volt distribution line. Current flowed through the metal edge strip, through Ozzie's right hand, through his left hand that was still holding the other edge strip, down the aluminum siding on the building façade, and then damaged all the appliances in the first-floor pizza restaurant.

The attorney asked him how he felt. "I was a little tired, so I took the rest of the day off," Ozzie told him. Some things cannot be explained; perhaps Ozzie has a guardian angel. Incidentally, Ozzie was not even a party to the lawsuit; the pizza guy was trying to collect for his appliances.

Case Study #4 – Smartphone Fire

A home was severely damaged by fire allegedly caused when a smartphone was left unattended while charging. The fire marshal and the other fire investigators had identified the origin of the fire to be in the vicinity of the phone. We were hired for the defense by the attorney of the manufacturer of the phone charger. As usual, we read through a lengthy case file, did some research, examined the evidence and an exemplar, and visited the scene. We couldn't find any defect, but we agreed with the information in the case file that the charger seemed to be the only item associated with the origin of the fire with enough energy to start the fire.

Then, somewhat by luck, we came across a news article about lithium-ion batteries catching on fire. We checked the specifications of the phone in question, and, sure enough, it had a lithium-ion battery. These batteries were becoming popular because of their high-density capacity (watt-hours/kilogram). A problem can occur if there is a failure of the thin separators that keep the elements of the battery apart. This can trigger what is known as "thermal runaway," causing the battery to overheat and burst into flames. Two things that keep today's lithium-ion batteries relatively safe are improvements in manufacturing techniques and the use of smarter monitoring systems. We also found an article about how these batteries can be damaged by using them in hot environments, causing rapid charging. Two of the depositions indicated that the phone was in front of the window on a carpet in direct sunlight.

Armed with this information, our attorney/client told us to stop all work on the case and to submit our final bill. The lessons here are keep abreast of the news related to your cases and find something else at which to point a finger.

Case Study #5 – Standard of Care

My largest forensic case involved the Denver International Airport. This was one of the largest construction projects in the United States for three years in a row and employed more than 10,000 workmen simultaneously. (I was not involved with the famous "Baggage Handling System" problems that delayed the opening of the airport for almost a year.) Because of what seemed to be an inordinate number of errors and omissions by the main terminal architects and engineers, the city and county of Denver decided to sue. Architects and engineers are not expected to be perfect and are not required to compensate owners for their mistakes, if these professionals meet the standard of care—"that level or quality of service ordinarily provided by other normally competent practitioners of good standing in that field, contemporaneously providing similar services in the same locality and under the same circumstances."

When my friends ask how I was selected to investigate the electrical issues, I tell them that they did a nationwide search and picked me. In fact, a mechanical engineer friend of mine met the litigation manager at a seminar and was asked to put together a New England team. I was told that they wanted to avoid anyone who might know the Denver architects and engineers.

I made six trips to Denver and reviewed files of 143 alleged electrical errors and omissions. I was deposed (oral questioning by the opposing attorney) for six hours and appeared on the witness stand for four hours. Unfortunately, there is no formula to apply regarding standard of care. I needed to evaluate the facts and circumstances and express my professional opinion.

The residents of Denver had endured the presence of rowdy construction workers for ten years and were anxious to get vengeance with a lawsuit. But by the time that the trial actually took place, they had all used the airport, enjoyed the wide concourses, and took pride in the many design awards that the airport received. Their verdict was "not guilty." An unofficial poll later revealed that the jurors' general feeling was "yes, they made a lot of mistakes, but it was a complicated and unique design and anyone would have made slipups."

Case Study #6 – Arc Flash Injury

This accident occurred when two electricians were troubleshooting an inoperative fan motor. They discovered a blown fuse in a 480-volt motor control center (a freestanding enclosure containing both fused switches and motor starters). They installed new fuses, closed the compartment door, tightened the screws holding the door, and closed the switch. An arc fault occurred in the compartment, which blew the door off, injuring both electricians. One had his clothes catch on fire resulting in third degree burns over 50% of his body. Both electricians were covered by "workman's compensation insurance," so they could not sue their employer. The more severely injured man sued the manufacturer of the motor control center. We were hired by his attorney to investigate.

First, we spent a lot of time looking through two big boxes of paperwork including information obtained from the manufacturer of the motor control center. Next, we did online research on the switchgear manufacturer's website and on the website of Underwriters Laboratory (UL). Then, we visited the site, examined the switchgear, and interviewed both electricians.

We observed that the spacing of the bus bars (live parts) within the enclosure appeared to be minimal and later compared this spacing to the details of other manufacturers of the same type of equipment, which confirmed our observation. We found numerous testing reports of the model switch at issue, and all ended in failures. We could not find any reports of switches that passed. However, we did find a letter from UL saying that the motor control center had qualified for "Follow up Services" which is a term used when equipment has passed initial testing and now can be manufactured with a UL listing and is subject to occasional inspections by UL. The UL Follow-Up Service program is designed to monitor the processes that a manufacturer uses to produce products in compliance with certification requirements. UL's field representatives make periodic tests and/or examinations at the factory, and may select samples from the factory, the open market or elsewhere for further determination of compliance. In addition, if a problem with a UL certified or classified product is reported to UL, UL will investigate these situations thoroughly.

Our "very happy" attorney/client called us two weeks later to tell us the case had settled. You don't necessarily need to testify to provide a valuable service.

Case Study #7 – Water Dispenser Fire

A name-brand appliance dispensed both hot and cold water. There were several reports of fires. The manufacturer had done extensive testing and was unable to find the cause of the fires. One of the burnt units was sent to us for examination and testing. The unit was severely damaged, and we could not find the problem. We requested an "exemplar" (new unit of the exact type). We took it apart, examined it, and tested resistances and continuity; again, we came up with no solution. Then, my lead investigator, Gary Hebner, read the manual word by word. One of the steps in the unpacking and setup procedures was to remove a plastic shipping plug. It was hard to find because it was made of the same yellow plastic material as the appliance. This plug prevented water from entering the heating compartment, thus causing the heating element to overheat the appliance. We then reexamined the burnt unit and discovered the burnt shipping plug. There are three important lessons here: ask for an exemplar, ask how long the damaged unit had been in operation, and, when all else fails, read the instructions.

Case Study #8 – Conveyor Accident

One of my cases involved a man who injured his hand on a conveyer in a sub-zero walk-in ice cream freezer. I was a defense witness for the electrician who (may have) installed the electrical system for the conveyor. My investigation revealed that the "conveyor code" required that a safety pull cord be installed above the conveyer that, if pulled, would stop the conveyor. It was not installed. It was my opinion that the conveyor manufacturer was responsible for ensuring that this safety device was installed. A representative of the manufacturer inspected the installation after completion and approved it for operation with no mention of the missing safety device. This pull cord is not a requirement of the National Electrical Code and was not referenced in the NEC at the time of installation. (Subsequently, a reference has been added.) Unfortunately, the conveyor manufacturer, who was also a defendant in the case, settled before the trial.

As I entered the courtroom, the injured man stuck out his left hand for a handshake. I was caught by surprise and probably looked startled and embarrassed. During the trial, the injured man sat up front next to his pretty wife while she held his withered hand.

I believe that I delivered my direct testimony clearly and conveyed my opinion of the case accurately. I feel that I stood up well under cross-examination. But, at the request of the plaintiff's attorney, the Judge directed me to stop referring to the defendant as "the electrician who may have installed the electrical work for the conveyor."

Regardless of the facts, it was not surprising that the jury awarded the plaintiff a huge monetary award.

Case Study #9 – Picking System Fire

A fire occurred at an office supply distribution center while they were in the process of having a "picking system" installed. A picking system is an electronic method of identifying products that were ordered. When an order is taken from a customer, a bar code for each item is recorded. The warehouse employee then scans the order, and an LED type display lights up on each bin that includes items ordered. This speeds up the picking process.

When we arrived at the appointed time for the site investigation, I was surprised by the number of attendees: forensic engineers, insurance adjusters, manufacturer's representatives, installer's representatives, and various people from the distribution center. The sign in sheet was 2 pages long. After an extensive meeting, we were allowed to view the scene of the fire in small groups; photography was permitted, but touching was not. In the afternoon, we viewed video surveillance of the actual start of the fire. The security surveillance camera was not close, was at a bad angle, and had poor resolution. But the fire appeared to start in the vicinity of one of the picking LCD screens. However, the fire spread so fast and the damage was so extensive that there wasn't much left. Before we left for the day, a group (representative of all parties) was designated to search through the trash. Fortunately, we were not selected.

We requested and received an exemplar of each part of the picking system, examined them, and did a few tests, to no avail. The wiring was all low voltage with proper ratings.

Shortly thereafter, we were told to stop all work and to submit our bill to date. I later heard a rumor that our "trash pickers" had found a broken and burnt light bulb in the trash, and it was thought to be the cause of the fire. But I never heard an official resolution of the case. Some cases just end, without notice of the outcome. But as long as they end with a check for final payment, that's okay.

OUTLINE SUMMARY

- **Forensic engineering:** "The application of the art and science of engineering in matters which are in, or may possibly relate to, the jurisprudence system."

- **Pros:** Interesting work, low liability, high hourly rates, little competition, and advanced payment via retainer.

- **Cons:** Can be stressful and sometimes requires travel.

- **Requirements:** Speaking/teaching ability, writing skills, willingness to prepare, and being a thorough reader.

- **Two types of witnesses:** A fact witness can only tell what they observed, not what others have said (hearsay) and not what they think concerning the case. On the other hand, an expert witness is a technical witness and can express opinions on matters within their expertise.

- **Expert witnesses:** Must be supportive of their opinions and not advocates for their attorney/client.

- **CV:** This is your expert witness resume and includes your present and previous company affiliations, positions and titles, education, certifications, PE licenses, memberships, awards, lectures, articles and papers published, and past forensic cases.

- **Marketing:** Send your CV to the litigation attorneys in your area with a cover letter introducing yourself, join the National Academy of Forensic Engineers (NAFE), contact the companies who frequently hire experts in your field, list in expert directories, and contact insurance companies.

- **Forensic fee agreements:** Should include an up-front, nonrefundable retainer, hourly rates, and a scope that retains you as a consultant until selected as the expert witness.

- **Investigations:** Include site inspections, interviews, examinations of evidence, testing, and reviewing of testing done by others. If you suspect that evidence has been tampered with or spoiled, immediately inform your attorney/client.

- **White papers:** Case preparation provides an opportunity to prepare narratives of specialized topics to use on future cases and as the basis of articles authored by you.

- **Your case file:** The first two pages should be your case summary and case time and charges.

- **Reports:** Do not write reports until your attorney/client requests. There are three basic types of reports: verbal, outline, and detailed.

- **Depositions:** Are "oral testimony, under oath, taken by the opposing attorney in advance of trial" and are often required of expert witnesses, especially if the case is expected to go to trial.

- **The trial:** The good news is that the vast majority of cases settle; the bad news is that you need to prepare every case as if it will go to trial. Review what to bring to court with your attorney/client. Usually, bring your CV, your fee schedule, time sheets, bills, case summary, and your report. Preparation is the key to success: write out questions and practice responding; try to appear confident, knowledgeable, and likable; consider exhibits and props; sit up straight and lean slightly forward; respond confidently to each question while looking at the jury; present a self-assured demeanor; and try not to let the opposing attorney get you visibly upset.

- **Cross-examination:** Most opposing attorneys are civilized. However, some of them can be nasty and abrupt in their cross-examinations. Craft answers to questions involving the following: your compensation, honesty, being correct, having read everything, having told everything, the reputation of the opposing witness, deleting information from your file, and your attorney/client having told you what to say.

- **Cases:** Accept only cases in your field of expertise, but don't necessarily limit them to your area of specialty. My cases as an electrical engineer included electrocutions, fires of suspected electrical origin, standard of care, equipment failures, arc fault accidents, conveyor accidents, lightning strikes, and others. Yours will be different but also interesting and challenging.

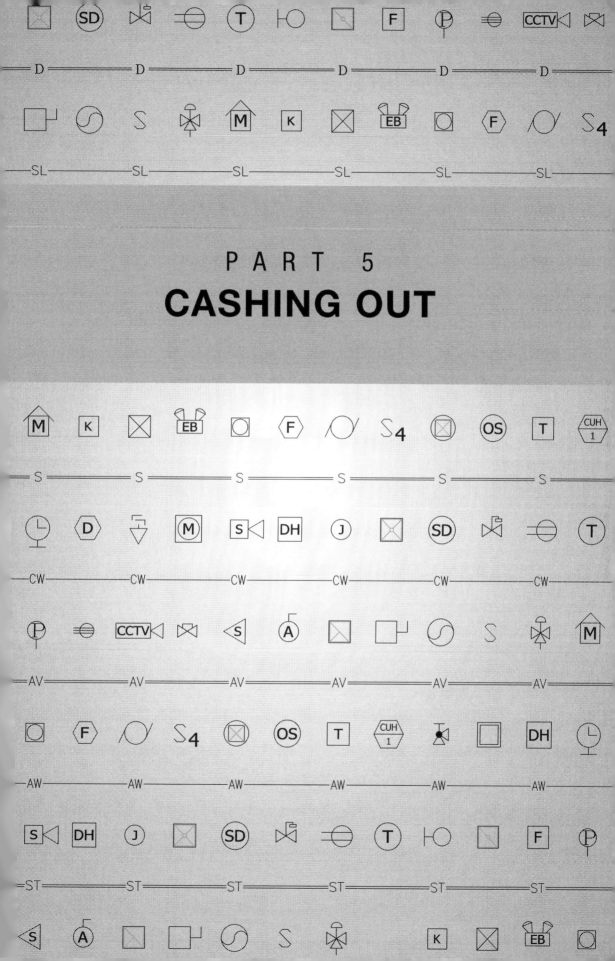

PART 5
CASHING OUT

CHAPTER 17

SELLING YOUR PRACTICE

INTRODUCTION

Discover how and when to start planning for retirement and when to actually do it. Learn the pros and cons of just closing, selling to relatives, selling to employees, forming an ESOP, selling to investors, selling to a local engineering firm, or marketing your practice nationally or internationally. Find out what factors determine what your firm is worth and how and where to get a valuation. Finally, determine step-by-step how to build your exit strategy.

WHEN IS IT TIME TO SAY GOODNIGHT?

Retirement is a tough decision for most engineers, especially those of us who work for ourselves and enjoy the work.

I started my engineering firm on my 29th birthday, and I had been practicing for roughly 35 years and loved my work. But I was approaching my mid 60s and knew that I should start thinking about and planning for retirement.

My mentor, John W. King, retired at age 70 upon the insistence of his wife. At that point, John's former trade school students were the prominent contractors bidding on our work. Whenever one of them would call about a job site problem, even on another engineer's project, John would drop everything, go to the site, and solve the problem, at no charge. During John's final years of practice, there were more than the normal number of "boo-boos." Some of these were because the new kid (me) was inexperienced; others were because John was slipping. But John's former students stepped up and donated the labor and materials to fix the mistakes, and John never had to pay a dime.

I decided not to wait for my declining years.

SELLING OPTIONS

To the amusement of my wife and children, when making major decisions, it has always been my practice to make a list of options and associated benefits and drawbacks. I think that this is a trait of most engineers.

I no longer have my list, but I think it looked something like the following:

Close the doors

Benefits:
This could be done over a number of years while cutting back on hours. It would allow a gradual transition while concentrating on the more interesting projects and the more enjoyable aspects of the work. There would be little concern about being bored because hours would be somewhat flexible. The final tasks would be "construction phase" services, which are usually less demanding. If money was not a factor, this might be the nicest transition choice.

Drawbacks:
Except for the eventual sale of the fixed assets, this option does not provide for a retirement *nest egg*. Also, with the closing of the practice, the company name and reputation ceases, which is a concern for some of us. Although if there were few or no employees, this may be the only viable option. The lasting value of a "service" business is its staff.

Another drawback is the likelihood that your staff will abandon you because they see that they will soon need a new job.

When an electrical engineer competitor of mine was winding down, his right-hand man approached me for a job. I knew that this guy would make a great addition to my staff. But I didn't want to see my competitor have difficulty completing his last few projects. So, I told the applicant to wait until he was no longer needed and there would be a job waiting for him with me. He eventually did come to work for me and was a good project manager. When my competitor finally retired, he visited all his clients to say good-bye and recommended my firm to each. Try to treat your competitors fairly and garner mutual respect.

As I related in Chapter 2, a mechanical engineer friend started his practice about the same time that I started mine. His work was exceptional and he made a good living, but he never had more than one drafter. When he retired, he laid off the drafter and closed the office.

By the time that I was considering retirement, we had grown to a staff of eleven, and I had something of value to sell.

Sell to family

Family situations are often awkward and unique. If your children are employed by your business, factors like professional standing and longevity need to be considered. Perhaps you should delay retirement until client loyalties and confidences are transitioned to your children and until they become PEs.

Benefits:

Your name and reputation will endure. This option could have many of the advantages of "closing the doors" and the satisfaction of providing your children an ongoing professional career.

Drawbacks:

It is difficult to charge family members the same price that you would expect an outsider to pay. They often feel entitled and may feel that they should inherit the firm because of their roll in its success. Siblings that are not part of the business will expect their fair share of the value of the firm. Each situation needs to be evaluated on its own merits, but there is a strong likelihood that someone will feel cheated.

My son came to work for me one summer. He had strong grades in math and science, and I thought he might become an engineer. But he lasted less than two weeks; I fired him after he had an argument with my senior associate. He is now a successful attorney in private practice with a partner. My daughter never had an interest in engineering and is now a trusted phlebotomist for a blood testing laboratory.

On many of my projects, I worked with a great mechanical consulting engineering firm; it included a father, two sons, and a grandson. Also, there were other children and grandchildren who were not in the business. I can only imagine the difficulties of ownership and ownership transition.

One of my largest architectural clients included an esteemed architect as the owner and one of his many children, an accountant, as the comptroller. When the architect father died, the son became president of the corporation. They have remained successful, but they are having some aggravation from the Board of Registration of Architects in a nearby state, who require that all officers of the corporation be members of the profession. I am sure that this was a complicated ownership transition.

Sell to employees

If you have employees who are PEs, they may be candidates to purchase your business.

Benefits:

Your existing employees and your clients already know each other and are used to working together. The existing relationship usually helps to make this kind of transition smooth and successful.

Drawbacks:

As with family, employees often feel entitled because of their contribution to the success of your firm and think that the price should be discounted. Also, they often lack the capital and/or credit needed. It might be necessary for you to accept a small down payment followed by monthly payments funded by future profits from the business. These payments depend upon the success of the new ownership and may not be secure if the company fails.

One of my best friends, a mechanical engineer, sold his practice to his employees and still receives monthly payments, even though the company has been resold.

Form an ESOP

ESOPs, "Employee Stock Ownership Plans," are often formed to give employees part ownership in the business over time for free as part of their overall compensation package. The benefits are improved employee relations, stability, and often lower borrowing costs. A disadvantage is that as more and more of the business becomes employee owned, less of the stock is available to the original equity holders to sell.

However, an ESOP can be formed as a method of selling your business to your employees. Simultaneously, you can also sell or gift a portion of your ownership to any other parties.

Benefits:

- Sale by ESOP is a "stock sale" and often provides substantial tax advantages to the seller.
- After the sale, the business can expense retirement plan contributions.
- If you choose to, you can retain operating control, even after the sale.

Drawbacks:

- Full cash payment, at closing, is rare.
- Lenders often require sellers to personally guarantee the loan for a period of time.
- Your eventual full payment is dependent upon the success of a company that you no longer manage.

If you pursue this method of selling your engineering practice, be sure to seek competent and experienced legal and business advice. This method usually works best for firms over 50 employees.

Sell to investors

Selling to investors is unusual, but is an option, especially for larger firms.

Benefits:

- It increases your pool of possible buyers.
- More likely to be an all-cash offer.
- Could be done with an ESOP sale.

Drawbacks:

- Your staff may not be willing to work for non-professionals.
- Future hiring may be impeded for the same reason.
- Outsiders might mismanage professional services.
- Outsiders might overlook the ethical requirements.
- This arrangement might violate Registration Board requirements.
- It is likely you would be required to stay on through the transition.
- PEs' personal liability might be an issue.

Combine with another local engineering firm

This is sometimes done by small firms as a way of easing into retirement. But the value that you offer is the clients that you would bring, your reputation, and fixed assets. These would not likely be substantial.

Sell to a local engineering firm

Benefits:

You and your reputation are more of a known entity to a local firm. They can more easily check you out because you both know many of the same people. It expands the buyer's customer base and technical talent. It may expand their services and/ or disciplines. It usually simplifies and consolidates management and services.

Drawbacks:

They may attribute less value to your company because you are not the unknown guys from more than 100 miles away.

Also, by marketing only locally, you may miss out on the extra value that a regional or nationwide company might pay to have a branch office in your area with an existing pool of satisfied clients.

Market the firm nationally

If the first several options mentioned above do not restrict you, I recommend that you market your firm both nationally and locally to both engineering firms and investors.

WHAT IS YOUR COMPANY WORTH?

The valuation of an engineering practice is a difficult and complex process, and it is not an exact science. Most engineering firms have few fixed assets. Basically, a firm's value is a function of the estimated "income stream" that it will generate in future years. Of course, no one knows the future, but there are some factors that are good indicators:

- How did your practice do financially over the past three years?
- We often hear that companies sell for a multiple of earnings. But what are earnings: gross profit, operating profit, net profit, or after tax profit?

- The firm's biggest assets are the number and competence of their technical staff. Are they happy and long term employees? Will they stay under the new ownership?
- Will your departure have a serious negative effect on moral, management, competence, and client relations?
- Has your firm developed specialized services with high profits that are likely to continue after you leave?
- Have you positioned the firm with unique skills or specialized services to give them an advantage for selection for future work?
- What is the overall standing of your firm? Have you developed a reputation for competence and quick and reliable service? Is the firm known widely, locally, statewide, regionally, nationwide, or internationally?
- Are you willing to stay on as an employee to help loyalties transition to the new owners?

MY TRANSITION

I wanted to leave gracefully with my good reputation still intact. I had many good friends in the industry, and I didn't want to rely on them to bail me out of any mistakes that I might make in my declining years.

I often went once a month to a breakfast meeting of consulting engineers and architects in Boston, MA. It was a first class meeting held at a fancy hotel near the harbor. It was sponsored by an E&O Insurance agency and was free (my favorite price). They have informative speakers on current topics of interest to A&Es. For me, it meant getting up before 5 am to drive to Boston through rush hour traffic. In retrospect, I am not sure that the value of the meetings were worth the risk of the journey. But I wanted to keep current and to possibly meet potential clients. I made it a point to arrive early, sit with a different group each month, exchange business cards, and try to make new contacts. At one of these meetings, I met a "little old man" (probably younger than I am now) who told me he was a business broker and was experienced doing A&E business valuations.

This chance meeting is probably what sparked my interest in finding out more about selling my company. I went to the bookstore, found a few good books on selling a business, and also bought a book on selling an engineering practice that I found from an advertisement in an engineering magazine. I did some reading and became more knowledgeable on the topic, but I had more questions than answers.

There were many ads in engineering magazines for business brokers who worked on a percentage fee basis. I finally came across an ad for a mergers and acquisitions firm offering to serve as an "advisor" for an hourly fee.

Eventually, I hired both this M&A firm and my "little old" friend to do an evaluation of my firm. They both signed a "non-disclosure agreement," and I provided all the financial and background information needed. One came in 40% higher than the other, but I figured that it gave me a range. As it turned out, my eventual sale price, including performance bonuses, was just about in the middle.

When I was ready, I hired the same mergers and acquisitions firm to serve as advisors for the sale of my practice. Together, we crafted a description of the firm: "Long established, highly reputable, New England electrical consulting engineering firm with staff of eleven for sale."

They sent a brief e-mail including this description to their nationwide list of potential buyers and then followed up—with no results.

I then went to the library and culled through the New England yellow pages for likely potential candidates for them to query—again, with no results.

Next, I contacted the most popular electrical industry magazine: EC&M. I rented their "electrical engineer" mailing list and sent a letter to each on my M&A firm's letterhead. There were several replies, but none that were interested enough to sign the non-disclosure agreement to receive the full package of information. I started to look for more mailing lists and considered magazine advertising.

In the meantime, I had continued to look for more local firms for my mergers and acquisitions firm to send e-mails to. I added a firm that I had heard of but knew nothing about: Thielsch Engineering. They responded, and I met Tom Lent, the President and CEO, at a restaurant for lunch. He is a great guy; we hit it off immediately and eventually completed the purchase and sale of my practice. Thielsch is a 500 person engineering firm made up of many unrelated engineering divisions. We became their 13th division; their first "buildings" division and I stayed on for 3 years to help establish the new division. We grew from 11 to 17 and became a multi-discipline firm by the time that I actually retired. Fortunately, I only have great things to say about Tom and Thielsch Engineering.

YOUR TRANSITION PLAN

Your plan for the sale of your engineering practice will depend upon your circumstances, plans, and, in part, the status and expectations of the economy at the time.

Here are my step-by-step recommendations:

- Review the selling options listed above, and determine what best suits your situation and desires.
- Do some research regarding mergers, acquisitions, and the selling of a professional practice. With the advent of the internet, this is now a lot easier to do.
- Contact several mergers and acquisition firms, and see what services they provide and what fees they charge, including options. After they give you an overall quote, request that they break it down into steps. Try not to commit to the whole package; instead, do it one step at a time.
- If you start early enough, an M&A firm may be able to analyze your practice and provide a written plan to position your company for sale in the future.
- In your last few years, contribute the maximum to your retirement plan to build it up while you can. In doing so, you will be contributing generously to your employees' retirement plans, but the alternative is paying more taxes.
- Get a minimum of 2 valuations, and carefully review the qualifications of both providers beforehand.
- In the absence of special restrictions, like family, both a local and nationwide search is probably advisable. The way that we are moving toward a global economy, an international search might not be out of the question.
- Consider specialized mailing lists and e-mail lists.
- The internet has websites and message boards where you can post for sale information; some of them appear to be free.
- Confidentiality is very important. Don't give out confidential information without an agreement provided by your M&A advisor or your attorney. Don't tell your staff, clients, or anyone else that you are thinking of selling. You don't want your staff or clients to abandon you or your competition to pirate them away.

With perseverance and a little luck, you will sell your consulting engineering firm for a fair, but maximum, price, and retire comfortably and enjoy your grandchildren, hobbies, and travel. Perhaps you will even write a book.

Enjoy retirement, you've earned it.

OUTLINE SUMMARY

- **Retirement:** Deciding when to retire is a difficult decision for most consulting engineers because the work is interesting and enjoyable. But do it while your reputation is still intact.

- **Options:**
  - **Close:**
    Pros: Gradual with flexible hours.
    Cons: Little final payout, staff may abandon you, and ends company name.
  - **Sell to family:**
    Pros: The pride of providing family a good living.
    Cons: Likely less payout and conflicts with siblings.
  - **Sell to employees:**
    Pros: Existing relationships smooth the way to success.
    Cons: Possible lack of cash/credit, and likely installment sale.
  - **Sell by ESOP:**
    Pros: Tax advantages, and leaves an employee retirement plan.
    Cons: Likely installment payments and personal guarantees.
  - **Sell to investors:**
    Pros: Increases buyer pool, likely all cash, and ESOP possible.
    Cons: Morale, ethics, PE Boards restrictions, your possible continued involvement, and liability.
  - **Sell to a local engineering firm:**
    Pros: Comfortable, and provides clients, staff, and specialties.
    Cons: Possibly lower sales price due to familiarity.
  - **Market the firm nationally:**
    Pros: Maximum sales price and local sale is still possible.
    Cons: Not an option for family or employee sales.

- **Price:** The value of your firm is based on the estimated "income stream" that it will generate in future years. This is indicated by past performance, specialized services, technical staff, special advantages, outstanding skills and reputation, speed and reliability of service, and your willingness to temporarily provide management/advice.

- **Your plan:** Your plan for the sale of your engineering practice will depend upon your circumstances, plans, and the status and expectations of the economy at the time.

- **Step-by-step recommendations:** Review the selling options; do some research; contact several mergers and acquisition firms and see what services they provide and what fees they charge, including options; start early and position your firm for a future sale; contribute the maximum to your retirement plan with company contributions; get a minimum of 2 valuations; do both a local and national search; consider specialized mailing lists and e-mail lists; and post on the internet. Confidentiality is very important.

- **Enjoy retirement:** You've earned it.

FORMS & ILLUSTRATIONS

AFTERWORD

One year after you have read this book and implemented some of my advice, let me know how you are doing. Are you happy in the field of consulting engineering? Are you successful in your own practice? Which of my advice worked best for you? Which of my counsel failed? What new items should I include in my next addition? If you found my guidance valuable, write a review and post it on Amazon.com and BarnesandNoble.com. Also, send the review to me so that I may "excerpt" it in my next addition or in my book promotion. If you didn't like the book, please tell me why. In any case, I wish you much continued success. Keep in touch.

INDEX

NOTES

Purchase additional copies of this book at a *discount*.
Go to https://TheEngineersResource.com
Enter coupon code: paperback

NOTES

NOTES

Purchase additional copies of this book at a *discount.*
Go to https://TheEngineersResource.com
Enter coupon code: paperback

NOTES

Purchase additional copies of this book at a *discount*.
Go to https://TheEngineersResource.com
Enter coupon code: paperback

36036839R00177

Made in the USA
Middletown, DE
10 February 2019